Books by John J. Floherty

TROOPERS ALL
MEN AGAINST DISTANCE
DEEP DOWN UNDER
SEARCH AND RESCUE AT SEA
GET THAT STORY!
HIGH, WIDE AND DEEP
OUR F.B.I.: An Inside Story
TELEVISION STORY
AVIATION FROM THE GROUND UP
WATCH YOUR STEP
FIVE ALARM: The Story of Fire Fighting
SHOOTING THE NEWS: Careers of the Camera Men
BEHIND THE SILVER SHIELD
WHITE TERROR
MEN AGAINST CRIME
FLOWING GOLD: The Romance of Oil
MONEY-GO-ROUND
SONS OF THE HURRICANE

DEEP
DOWN
UNDER

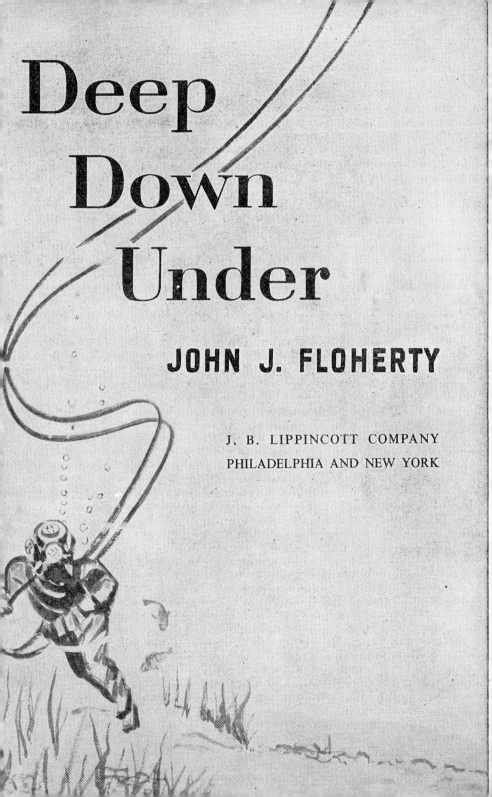

Deep Down Under

JOHN J. FLOHERTY

J. B. LIPPINCOTT COMPANY
PHILADELPHIA AND NEW YORK

The Author's Side of the Story

It has been my privilege to see a close-up of America at work.

There was only one trade, profession or cult, if you will, in which I found the members to be a silent brotherhood, hesitant to say a word not backed by cold fact. They were the divers.

Perhaps their reticence is due in part to the solitude in which they work. Or perhaps it results from the grave responsibilities that go with their job. They alone can appraise the character and extent of a project on the bottom, be it salvage or construction. They carry on in a dim twilight and often in complete darkness where sensitive fingers must substitute for sight.

Once during an interview I asked a diver why he chose working under water rather than in a less hazardous trade or profession. His reply was typical: "I don't have a boss looking over my shoulder, telling me how to do this or that."

Even in the other branches of diving that include Aqualungers, Frogmen, Mask and Fin swimmers, etc., I met with this same close-mouthed attitude. It was a friend, an ardent underwater sportsman of some fame in the Mediterranean, who enlightened me on the diver's antipathy to discussing his exploits. He said, "Why bother to tell folks about something they refuse to believe?"

I am deeply indebted for photographs and valuable data to the U.S. Navy, Merritt Chapman & Scott Corporation, Standard Oil, New Jersey and Lieutenant Commander Joseph Gibbons, U.S.N.R.

J. J. F.

CONTENTS

Illustrations following page 84

DEEP
DOWN
UNDER

1   PEARLS AND PERILS

"Nice mornin'!"

It was the crusty voice of old Captain Matt Cullen.

"Perfect," I replied, turning around to greet my elderly friend and occasional fishing partner.

Despite his years Captain Matt was sturdy as an oak, ruddy and rotund. His visored cap was cocked at an angle.

"Guess I'll bring this old hulk to an anchor," he said as he sat himself down on the stringpiece of the Town Dock. I joined him.

Before us was one of the most picturesque harbors along the Atlantic coast. Without a breath of wind to ruffle its surface Manhasset Bay lay like a two-mile mirror between Port Washington and Great Neck. Hundreds of pleasure craft lazed at their moorings.

"Look yonder!" exclaimed Captain Matt, pointing with the stem of his pipe. "The gulls are working off King's Point. Looks as if there was plenty of bait, and where there's bait, there's usually stripers. If it wasn't for this blamed leg of mine, I'd be out there in two shakes of a mackerel's tail." With his malacca cane he tapped his leg below the knee; it gave off a dull metallic sound.

"I've never asked you before," I said, "but how did you lose your leg?"

"Shark!" he replied. "A regular man-eater. And to make matters worse, when I lost my leg, I also lost a fortune, a pearl large as a robin's egg and as beautiful as a harvest moon. Worth a king's ransom. Right now it's a pendant in the neckpiece of one of the world's richest matrons. I believe they call it 'Luna,' you know, the moon."

"Would you tell me how it all happened?" I asked.

The captain paused as if probing his memory and then began: "You see I was in the pearl fishing business for many years. I owned a couple of sloops and employed a score or more of native boys as divers. We were fishing in the Sulu Archipelago off New Guinea where pearling is a staple business.

"Now those oyster beds where we gathered pearls had been worked for many years and were beginning to give out. So I decided to up anchor and head for a small uninhabited island to the eastward. It was sheltered from the trade winds and offered safe harbor in storms. Altogether it looked promising. We dropped anchor in some fifty feet of water.

"There's no sense in sending your boys down till you know what the chances are of profitable diving. That's why I always made it a point to have a look-see on the bottom before beginning operations. So I went over the side on a weighted line and landed right in the middle of a large growth of the finest oysters I had ever seen. They clung in such clusters to the volcanic rock, I could tell the bed had never been fished. Probing around in the green twilight, I came on one that was as large and fine as any ever found. Just as I had pried it loose, a faint shadow moved slowly along the bottom. I looked upward and sure enough, there was a shark circling leisurely above me. I could see his jaws working and his gills pulsating as he gulped and expelled the water. Grasping the pearl oyster in one hand, I swam for the line some fifteen feet away.

"Now sharks are strange critters that seem to be little understood even by those who make a study of fish. 'Icthyologists,' I believe they are called. Sometimes the shark is timid as a minnow. It will dart away as if in deadly fear of the diver. Again it will snoop around where the diver is working as if full of curiosity and suddenly slip off into the shadows. Once in a while it will attack savagely and for no apparent reason unless it be hunger. Now it is a strange fact that the number of known cases of death or injury by shark-bite is comparatively small. Even the United States Navy believes that the shark is much less dangerous than he is supposed to be. And yet, when vessels are in shark-infested waters, the Navy takes every precaution to protect its men against attack. During World War II it issued shark-repellent chemicals to men who were likely to be forced to swim. Now and then a renegade shark turns to man-eating. Human bones have been found in shark's bellies, but whether the victims were dead or alive when attacked has never been proved.

"These and a hundred other thoughts flashed through my mind during the few strokes I took to my life-line. I figured I'd been under some fifty seconds. No sooner had I grasped the line when the shark made a pass at me. I could see the two rows of teeth as he flashed by. I gave the line several sharp tugs, the signal to haul me up quickly. To have a free hand to use my knife, I dropped the precious oyster. Life was more valuable than the pearl it might hold.

"Clutching the life-line with my left hand and winding my left leg around it, I felt the sharp rapid tugs from the vessel above me as I was hauled up. I was thankful. But my hope and thanks were short-lived. I saw through the green haze the ghostly form of the shark approaching. He was on his side, his jaws wide open, his row on row of teeth bared. I ducked low and struck outward and upward with my knife hand. I could feel the sharp blade slice through the soft white belly. The shark swerved away. A swipe of his tail nearly knocked me senseless.

"My allotted underwater seconds were running out and I would have given the world for a deep breath. Ascent on the line seemed painfully slow. I could have swum to the surface much more quickly. I decided, in case of another attack, the line might come in handy. It was a lucky decision. When I had reached within a few feet of the surface, there was a flash of silver and gray. It struck with the speed of an arrow. The impact would have torn me from the line if I hadn't taken the precaution to put a couple turns of it around my wrists. A terrible pain shot up my right side. It was followed by a strange numbness below the knee. Then I passed out.

"When I came to, I was dazed and exhausted. My mate and two of the native boys were working over me. We were already under way for one of the nearby islands where there was a missionary doctor. Tender care and medical knowledge pulled me through, but my pearling days were over.

"Fortunately I had put aside a tidy sum that has enabled me to retire and live in this peaceful village where the tang of the sea is in the air and where folks know the bow of a boat from the stern."

"What about that valuable pearl you mentioned?" I inquired.

"Oh that!" he answered with a wry little smile. "My hard luck was the other fellow's good fortune. The day after we had left the scene of my encounter with the shark, another pearler came along and anchored in the very spot we had occupied. During the first half hour of diving one of his boys discovered the oyster I had dropped. It was lying loose on a cluster of shell."

"How could you know it was the same one?"

"That's easy," he replied. "An oyster spends nearly its entire life cycle firmly attached to a rock, another shell or any solid object. It can neither swim nor crawl nor move itself from where it is anchored. Let me explain:

"When spawning, an oyster produces from ten to sixteen million eggs that soon develop into tiny larvæ. These little creatures swim about at will for several days until the shell begins to form. Then they attach themselves to some convenient surface and remain there for life. No bigger than a pinhead, the tiny oyster, now known as a 'spat,' proceeds to make its residence permanent. It exudes a limey deposit that literally cements it to the object on which it rests. This process continues during the growth of the shell. When full grown it takes considerable force to dislodge it.

"So you see, an oyster lying loose on the bottom proved clearly that it had been pried from its original bed and dropped by someone.

"I knew from looking at the bed before I was attacked that it had never been disturbed by man. There was not the slightest doubt that the shell picked up by the native diver was the one I had dropped during my battle with the shark. That was conceded by all hands, but the law of the pearlers, 'Finders, keepers,' is adamant.

"The pearl embedded in the disputed oyster was one of unusual size and beauty. It was purchased by a Hindustani buyer for two thousand rupees, about seven hundred dollars. It passed through several hands before it was sold in London for fifteen thousand dollars. I have no idea what its value is today."

Captain Matt Cullen was silent for a moment or two. Then with a sigh of resignation, he said, "Oh well, I'm the winner! After all, I'd rather have my life than the pearl."

During the pause that followed I asked, "Of all the occupations open to a young man, how did you ever get into pearl fishing?"

"Well," replied the captain, "it's a strange story. But if you want it—" the captain tilted his cap back on his poll until it touched the nape of his neck, knocked the heel from his pipe and went on—"When I graduated from high school, I was all set for medicine. After a year at Columbia University I ran into the brother of a friend. He was a nice young fellow, mate on a four-masted bark, the *West Wind*.

"His tales of adventure and, at times, hardship somehow intrigued me. To make a long story short, I shipped out as foremasthand on the *West Wind*, bound for Sydney, Australia.

"It was a fair voyage as voyages go until we neared the Barrier Reef a hundred miles or so off the coast of Australia. There we were caught in a typhoon that left us a helpless wreck on the reef. For nearly eighteen hours we were battered by high seas and a sixty-mile wind. Seven of the crew, caught on the forward part of the vessel, were lost. Five of us survived.

"The deck was awash, a mill-race of mad water. Those of us who survived were hanging on in the weather rigging of the main- and mizzen-masts.

"At sundown the wind flattened out. Heavy swells rolled lazily over the wreck. In the morning two more men were missing—passed out from sheer exhaustion. At daybreak we were sighted by a trading schooner from the islands. With some difficulty and fine boatmanship we were taken on board. The master, Nils Nordhof, born to the sea, was tough as rawhide and shrewd as they come. Yet he had a friendly streak in a rough sort of way.

"One evening soon after we had come on board, he came to the fo'cs'le while we were at mess. 'Hey you!,' he said to me gruffly, 'I want to see you aft.' Now even on a trading schooner the captain's cabin is hallowed ground to the crew. I couldn't for the life of me figure why the skipper should ask me to come there.

"I found the captain's quarters as neat and orderly as if they had been presided over by a good housewife. There was one object, however, that seemed out of place—a shiny safe with the American manufacturer's name in gilt letters.

" 'Have a seat!' the captain said, pointing to a comfortable chair. Then he began to question me about my past, my home life, my education, my reasons for going to sea and my plans for the future.

"When we had talked for more than an hour, he paused in deep thought and said, 'Of course, you know we're bound for Brisbane. I've got a lot of business to attend to when we reach port—buying, selling and all that sort of thing. Trading with the natives calls for a large stock of goods and trinkets

of all kinds. Last voyage we carried three thousand dollars'
worth. We hit only the smaller islands where nearly all business is done by barter."

"What do you get in exchange for your goods?" I asked
Captain Nordhof.

" 'Pearls!' he said proudly as he patted the shiny safe. Then
he added, 'You look like a bright young fellow. I think I
could use you as a kind of supercargo to keep track of stock
and the business end of the ship. I'm not much of a hand
for figures. How about signing on?'

" 'Okay!' I said and right there began a warm friendship
that lasted two years.

"Now the skipper was a lonely man. He remarked many
times that to his knowledge he didn't have a living relative.
I believe that was why he took a fatherly interest in me.
Sometimes when he made a good sale of pearls in Brisbane,
he handed me a five-pound note, saying, 'Go ashore and have
a good time. But be sure you're back on board before dark!'
Once he handed me an envelope. On the flap was a great
blob of sealing wax with an impression on it of the seal ring
he always wore. 'I want you to know where I keep this,' he
said, 'just in case anything should happen to me!' He took
from the tiny book-shelf above the safe a copy of Bowditch,
opened it at random and placed the envelope between the
pages. I noticed with a shudder that the page was number
thirteen, a number for which he had a superstitious hate.

"Thirteen days later, during a heavy blow, he was caught
by a vicious boarding sea and hurled along the deck. His head
struck the pump at the foot of the mainmast with crushing
force. He died within a few hours of a fractured skull and
other injuries. We gave him Christian burial at sea.

"When the weather had moderated that evening, I went
aft to the cabin. Somehow in spite of its comfortable furnish-

ing and orderly neatness, it seemed desolate. I took from the shelf the copy of Bowditch in which the captain had placed the sealed envelope. Opening it, I read the contents of the single sheet it contained. It was a crudely written but properly witnessed last will and testament in which I was named the sole heir of all Captain Nordhof's worldly possessions. In a postscript was given the combination of the safe.

"Though deeply grieved at the skipper's death, I could not help feeling a certain elation over my good fortune. A bit bewildered, I sat thinking, absorbed in the strange turn of events and in what my future course should be.

"One of the crew, a West Indian, entered. He had acted as mate for several years. Illiterate, he held no ticket. Esposito, that was his name, had proven himself not only honest and reliable but as fine a sailor man as I had ever known. Once a pearl diver, he knew the islands and the pearling business like a book. 'Now where do we stand?' he asked me anxiously.

"I read him Captain Nordhof's will.

" 'That's good!' he said. 'Very good!' and without further comment he went on deck.

"The shiny safe taunted me. I didn't relish probing into a dead man's affairs. My hand trembled as I turned the knob of the combination. When I swung open the heavy door, the safe seemed to be almost empty. A small bundle of papers held together by a rubber band contained bills of sale, receipts, half a dozen letters and records of various transactions that had to do with ship's business. A teakwood case held a fine sextant that apparently had never been used. A cigar box contained a few pieces of jewelry, none of them valuable. In a closed compartment I found a dozen small white cardboard boxes, each about the size of a pack of playing cards. I opened one and gasped—a dozen pearls of unusual beauty nestled on a layer of soft cotton. All were identical in size and color.

In each of the other boxes were pearls of varying sizes but of fine lustre and texture. Here was a fortune that, for the moment, I could not believe was mine. In the lower compartment of the safe was a battered shoe-box. Opening it casually, I was stunned to find several bundles of Bank of England notes, nearly a thousand pounds in all. At that time they had a value of about five thousand dollars American.

"Naturally I was bewildered by the turn things had taken. I called Esposito.

"When I had shown him the contents of the safe, he merely pursed his lips, shrugged his shoulders and said, 'Good! very good!!'

" 'But Esposito!' I said, all confused, 'What are we to do now?'

"After a moment's silence he replied with hands outstretched, 'Trading no good for greenhorns. We head for the islands. We fish for the pearls. No more we trade for them.'

"Luckily for me, in my two years at sea, Captain Nordhof had taught me navigation and practical seamanship as thoroughly as if I were his own son. Esposito had long since proved himself a master hand at working ship, and besides, he knew pearl divers from the Fiji Islands to the Bay of Bengal. Also he knew the spots where pearls were to be found.

"We made a quick run to Brisbane where we met with the agent who for years had dealt with Captain Nordhof in the business of pearls and shell. The agent was shocked to hear of the captain's death. Besides buying part of our store of pearls, he attended to the legal aspect of the captain's will. He also deposited to our account in a local bank the cash we had on hand.

"Within six months we were well established in the pearl fishing business and had employed some of the best divers in the Pacific.

"Ever since I was a kid I had been a better than average swimmer. Now I was carried away by a desire to become a diver in my own right. Esposito frowned upon it. 'Leave diving to the divers,' he advised. 'That's their business. You stick to yours.'

"One day Butch, one of our best divers, was suffering with ear trouble—a common complaint in pearling when diving is deeper than sixty feet. This warning should have stopped me. But I ordered a boat crew to lower me on a weighted line. I filled my lungs several times and swallowed hard as I had seen the divers do. Before I submerged, one of the boatmen, formerly a diver, whispered to me, 'If ears hurt, pinch nose, shut lips and blow hard.'

"The descent was slow but steady. As I neared the bottom I was in a dim greenish twilight where objects were barely visible for about a boat's length. The coral bottom had formed in fantastic shapes. Patches of sea vegetation waved lazily. A shoal of brightly colored fish swam by, completely ignoring me. A giant crab scuttled off into the shadows. I took a few strokes away from the line and a long tendril of seaweed slithered along my body. It gave me the creeps. The breath I held in my lungs was beginning to hurt. I released it in short burps and the escaping air bubbles thundered in my ears. My heart was pounding like a trip hammer. I would have given the world for a good deep breath.

"After swimming around for a moment or two, my ears began to hurt, my head felt as if it were being squeezed in a vise, my sight became blurred. I reached for the line and gave it three sharp tugs. When I was hauled to the surface, I held on to the gunwale of the boat and gulped the fresh salty air.

" 'How long was I under?' I gasped.

" 'Thirty seconds,' Butch said. 'You no diver.'

"Although he never owned a watch, Butch could tick off

the seconds accurately as any chronometer. Even before I scrambled into the boat, I decided then and there to stick to diving until I could do at least as well as the average native.

"It took a whole year of diving before I could hold my breath for a minute under water. That was about average for the native divers. In the meantime I had learned some of the secrets of the professionals."

"What are some of those secrets?" I asked.

Captain Cullen's face wrinkled in a knowing smile. "When the water is deep," he replied, "the pearl divers work only when their stomachs are empty. That permits a greater expansion of the lungs and diaphragm and a greater volume of stored air. Even when out of water, their breathing is deep and full. When swimming, they streamline their bodies to save the last ounce of energy. Even a projecting toe may create a drag that will shorten their stay under water.

"In very deep water the pressure on the eardrums sometimes becomes unbearable. Pinching the nostrils and blowing hard with lips tight and throat open help to equalize the pressures in the inner and outer ear. The relief, however, is only temporary. Many divers suffer from ruptured eardrums, and sometimes become partially or totally deaf."

"How long can a pearl diver stay under water?"

"I've known cases where a diver remained submerged for ninety seconds. And I've heard of two and even three minute dives. From my own experience I'm inclined to doubt the latter."

"How deep can those pearl divers swim?"

"That too," the captain replied, "is debatable. As a rule pearl fishing is done in only moderately deep water, say, from thirty to sixty feet. But there are cases we know of in which, without any of the modern appliances like flippers or goggles, nose-clamps or portable air supply, divers have swum to a depth of more than a hundred feet in their search for the valuable black mother-of-pearl shell. The Polynesians of the Tuamotu Islands are reported to have made dives as deep as twenty-five fathoms—one hundred and fifty feet. I'm afraid I take those reports with a grain of salt. There is, however, indisputable evidence that these Polynesian natives salvaged a two-hundred-pound anchor at a depth of one hundred and twenty-five feet."

"Tell me, captain," I said, "how are pearls formed and from what do they come?"

"I'm no scientist," he answered, "so I take the word of men who have spent their lives in the study of pearls and the shellfish in which we find them. These fish line the inside of their shells with layer on layer of a crystalline substance called 'nacre,' which chemically is carbonate of lime. This coating, commercially known as mother-of-pearl, is almost exactly like a pearl in its composition. When a grain of sand or some other irritating substance is sucked in by an oyster during feeding, it lodges between the oyster's soft body and the shell. The oyster begins at once to coat the irritant with nacre. The oyster keeps the coated particle rolling constantly and so gives the growing pearl perfect symmetry.

"Centuries ago the Chinese, aware of the oyster's secret of producing valuable pearls, inserted small particles of bone between the shells and so established an industry that has flourished through the years—the culture of pearls."

"Does the growth of the pearl affect the health of the oyster?" I asked.

"It certainly does. A pearl-bearing oyster is usually unhealthy. Its shell is distorted often to the point of deformity. Its flesh is flabby and undernourished. The larger the pearl, the poorer the oyster's condition. This holds true also of freshwater mussels of the pearl-bearing variety."

"Is it true," I inquired, "that valuable pearls have been found in oysters served in restaurants or in the home?"

"No!" he snapped. "The occasional pearl found in an edible oyster is of little or no value beyond being a curiosity. Commercial pearls, those with the texture and luster that make them valuable, are found chiefly in the 'Aviculidâe' or pearl-oysters which because of their coarse flesh, are considered inedible. Genuine pearls of considerable value are found also in fresh-water mussels. They are prized for the beautiful variety of their color."

"And now, captain, will you tell some of your experiences while in the pearl fishing industry?"

After a minute, he said, "I remember once off the Australian coast one of my divers reported finding on the bottom a metal chest that apparently had lain there a long time.

"I decided to go down and look it over. The depth was about sixty feet. A heavy bottom growth, waving in a gentle current, made my search difficult. I found the chest, however, on the second dive; and sure enough it had the appearance of a treasure chest similar to those the old shipmasters used to hold their valuables. It was partially sunk in the sandy bottom and encrusted with young oysters that had 'struck' on it. Corrosion had partly eaten away the handles on the ends but the strap hinges and lock fastenings seemed sound.

"At sixty feet you can't work for very long. It took nearly two days for two of the boys and myself to dislodge it from its bed and rig lines on it to hoist it to the surface. Once safely on the deck of the schooner, the ancient chest sent hopes soaring into dreams of rich treasure. 'Graved on the lid was the ship's name now corroded so that only three letters were decipherable—V-A-L. After long labor with cold chisel and hammer we opened it and found not treasure but a soggy mass of what once had been richly embroidered clothing clinging to the skeleton of an infant that could not have been more than a year old. Among the debris of little bones was a tiny cross of gold—obviously a talisman that had failed. It indicated, however, that the child had received Christian burial at sea.

"Sancho, our number one diver who found the little trinket, insisted on keeping it as a luck-piece. He hung it on a piece of sail twine around his neck. Two days later while making a dive in fifty feet of water, he failed to surface on time. Fearing trouble, I went down to investigate. Sancho was nowhere in sight. While searching the bottom I saw a small object gleam in the underwater twilight. It was the little cross. Knowing it would rouse the superstition of the natives if I took it on board, I left it undisturbed. Despite hours of lung-busting search, we never found Sancho. Sharks, I suspect.

"Now Sancho had a son. We called him Bud. Native names were hard to remember, so we gave the boys nicknames. Bud was a smart lad of about nineteen and popular with all hands. As a diver, he could hold his own with the best of them. He was known to stay under a minute and a half on several occasions. Another of the boys we called Bucky, somewhat older than Bud, was morose with a strong streak of jealousy. There seemed to be bad blood between the two. One morning while we were working over a rich bed in about forty feet, Bud and Bucky seemed to be on unusually bad terms.

"Esposito came aft, his face puckered with anxiety. Pointing amidships with his thumb over his shoulder, he growled, 'Plenty trouble makin' up!' Glancing forward, I could see nothing amiss. The two young divers were clambering over the side and into the canoe they used to work from, scarcely a dozen paddle strokes from the schooner. Perhaps it was Esposito's fear of trouble that made me watch the lads as they dove under. While Bucky filled his lungs I saw hatred in his coal-black eyes. As the water closed over him I noticed his right arm as if reaching for the knife held in his G string. Suspecting foul play, I dropped over the side and swam with everything I had to where I'd find the boys on the bottom. When I was about twenty-five feet from them, I saw dimly a tangle of flailing, writhing legs and arms and twisting torsos, with a glint now and then from a knife blade as it caught the light from above. In savage embrace each held a death grip on the wrist of the other's knife hand.

"Swimming on my back with knees drawn up almost to my chin, I approached the infuriated men cautiously. Seeing an opportunity, I let drive with my feet and caught Bucky squarely on the jaw. Stunned, he dropped his knife. Great globs of air burbled from his mouth as he settled on the coral bottom.

"Between us, Bud and I got him to the surface quickly as possible, and none too soon, for scarcely had we laid him on the deck when the dorsal fin of a huge shark was seen circling the vessel. Artificial respiration soon brought Bucky back to consciousness and a seemingly chastened spirit. Although I questioned both boys, I could get no light on the cause of the vendetta. One night about two weeks later, while we were anchored off a small and remote island, Bucky slipped over the side. The shore was a good quarter mile away. Maybe he reached it and maybe he didn't. We never saw him again."

Here Captain Cudden paused as he watched a commercial fishing boat pass by. On the afterdeck one of the crew was deftly opening clams and dropping their juicy content into a large pot.

"Looks like it's clam chowder for all hands," I remarked.

The captain frowned. "Don't mention clams to me!" He growled. "The mere word sends a chill through my marrow.

"Yes, *sir*," the captain continued. "I saw one of my best divers die in the grip of a clam, a giant clam, while I was powerless to help him. We were pearling off the coast of New Guinea and by sheer luck struck a bed of valuable black shell about seventy feet down. Spirits ran high. In black shell you find the prized black pearls. We had found several beauties.

"Perhaps it was because of our good luck that Mamba, my best deepwater boy, decided to make one more dive after the others had quit. As he went over the side, I thought he showed signs of fatigue. Scarcely had he gone under when I regretted I had let him make the dive. I reasoned, however, that Mamba could always take care of himself. I began to tick off the seconds mentally. When a minute had passed I became anxious. Esposito whispered to me, 'Mamba in trouble!'

"Instantly I was over the side and on my way down. I swam close to the bottom and caught sight of him near a low overhanging coral shelf that was partly screened by a growth of sea cabbage. He was struggling violently as if fighting off an invisible enemy. I grasped his shoulder. As he turned his head I could see terror in his eyes. Then I discovered that his right foot, hidden in the sea growth, was held firmly by something underneath. Investigating, I found it gripped in the scalloped shell of a giant clam that had snapped shut on his ankle with all the power of a bear-trap.

"Seconds were running out. I slashed my knife deep into the pulpy flesh of the clam in the hope it would release its grip. My effort merely made it squeeze more tightly. Grasping Mamba's hand, I added my force to his in a futile effort to pull the foot free.

"It was then I noticed that his strength was failing rapidly. I knew that in a matter of a few seconds it would be all over. With a burst of hidden energy he made a convulsive effort to free himself, then collapsed. A slender string of air bubbles —the last reserve of air in his lungs—went hurrying up to the surface. Mamba was dead, the victim of a clam!

"It took several hours and several divers to recover the body. With its victim still in its grip, we pried the giant clam loose from its lair and hoisted both to the deck of the schooner. Not until the huge shell had been smashed with a sledge hammer was the lifeless Mamba freed."

A bit horrified by the captain's tale, I asked, "Just how large was that clam?"

"Believe it or not, it weighed four hundred pounds and was about as big as a washtub. A number of giant clams found in the Pacific have weighed more than five hundred pounds and those I'll wager, are small when compared with the monster clams that lie in the greater depths where divers never dare venture."

By way of changing the gruesome subject, I inquired, "How large do pearls grow?"

"Commercial pearls," he replied, "range from the size of marbles down to the size of small bird-shot. There have been found, however, rare pearls of great size. There's the famous Pearl of Asia taken from the Persian Gulf during the early part of the seventeenth century. It measures three inches in diameter, and while not spherical is of surpassing luster. It was presented by Shah Johan, a Mogul Emperor, to his beautiful wife, Mumtag Mahal. Soon afterward Mumtag died and the Shah built a tomb for her, the Taj Mahal, often mentioned as the most beautiful building in the world.

"A hundred years later another East Indian potentate gave the fabulous pearl to the Chinese emperor, Ch'ien Lung. In nineteen hundred the Pearl of Asia was stolen from the emperor's tomb. All trace of it was lost for many years until a missionary bought it for a few hundred rupees. Today it is mounted in a setting of gold, jade, quartz and a smaller but priceless pearl, and it is one of the world's most treasured jewels."

"Has modern diving equipment been adopted by native pearl divers?" I asked.

"Only where pearling is done on a large scale," he said. "Diving apparatus is expensive and so is its operation. The services of several men are required so that a professional diver can work on the bottom in safety. In most cases air is supplied him by a hand pump. In large operations air comes from a power-driven air compressor. Then the diver must have a 'tender' to handle his lines. Burdened with the massive weight of his equipment, the diver has little freedom of movement when out of water. In the water he must be lowered and raised as if he were a heavy boulder. Then too there must be men to haul up the shell the diver loads into a heavy metal basket. All in all it is a cumbersome but efficient way to gather pearls and shell.

"Yet even in pearling, deep-water diving equipment has its advantages. The diver can work in comparative comfort at great depths and for long periods. But give me the native boy born to the water. His knowledge of the undersea is inherited from generations of divers. The native boy knows his way around under the surface just as a seasoned cop knows his beat."

"How many pearl oysters can a diver get during an average day?" I inquired.

"A good diver will bring up about a hundred and fifty oysters during a day's work. With several hundred divers working in a fleet, a season's take amounts to about two thousand tons of oysters yielding pearls and shell valued at about half a million dollars. The northwest coast of Australia has become one of the richest sources of the best quality pearls and mother-of-pearl. Annual exports from that area are valued at about two million dollars."

"How do fresh-water pearls compare with those taken from the sea?"

"Fresh-water mussels produce pearls of great variety and beauty of color. They're found in huge quantities in the Mississippi Valley and are secured mostly by rakes, tongs and sometimes steam dredges. The discovery of pearl-bearing mussels in some localities has caused on several occasions a rush of excited pearl hunters like the gold rushes of the old days."

Here the captain drew from his breast pocket an old-fashioned watch and looked at the time. It was noon. "Bless my soul!" he exclaimed. "Grub is ready! And the wife is waiting. Guess I'll have to shove off."

As he departed, I noticed that the old pearl fisher walked faster and limped less than when he arrived. Dwelling on his adventurous past seemed to have lightened the load of his years.

2   FROGMEN

Even while I chatted with Captain Cullen I began to wonder when and where and why men first invaded the bottom of the sea. What was their objective? What was their reward?

Many hours of research failed to reveal the origin of man's mastery of the art of staying under water for varying periods and for various purposes. Then one day I ran into an old friend at the American Museum of Natural History. He had just returned from an expedition to the waters off the coast of Central America. His mission: to collect specimens of various types of marine algæ, or seaweed, from their natural habitat on the bottom.

Like many scientists I have known, he grew eloquent when embarked on his favorite subject. He was enthralled by the weird beauty of the undersea floor. He described the rich color and fantastic forms of the bottom growth as ardently as a garden club member might describe the dazzling beauty of blooms and plants at a flower show.

Familiar only with the drab and withered seaweeds I had often seen washed up on the beaches, particularly after a storm, I remarked, "But aren't those seaweeds, or algæ as you call them, more or less colorless?"

He fairly bristled. "On the contrary," he declared, "they quiver with color that ranges from light pink to deep red and from delicate lavender to sombre purple. There are greens so vibrant no painter could capture them. There are vistas that can be seen through the diaphanous curtain of tropical sunlight that streams down through crystal-clear water, that are breath-taking for beauty of color and grace of motion."

"Motion?" I queried.

"Yes," he said, "true poetry of motion. You must remember that in the water as in the air there is constant movement. The mere flick of a tail by a passing fish will set the long ribbons of sea grass and the delicate fronds of the various algæ waving and curtseying and gyrating as if directed by a ballet master. Then too, because they are lighter than the volume of water they displace, they try to stand straight in obedience to the laws of gravity. I have seen seaweeds rising a hundred feet so that their fronds carpet the surface of the sea. On land these same growths would lie as limp as a tangle of wet string.

"In many places the bottom is encrusted with a heavy layer

of organic matter, some of it living, some of it fossilized over the ages, and all of it stippled with glowing color in which red, green and deep violet predominate. Brightly-hued fishes, singly and in schools, swim lazily out of nowhere and disappear into the dim vastness. Surface ripples throw quivering shadow patterns dappled with sunlight over everything below. Occasionally a large and sinister shadow glides silently over the bottom. It is a moment for alarm, since sharks are always the number one menace. Strange creatures, these sharks! You never know whether they mean business or whether they're just making a friendly call."

"What type of diving equipment do you use in your work?" I asked.

"Since few species of algæ are found at depths of more than sixty or seventy feet, much of our work is done in comparatively shallow water. Consequently our equipment is almost rudimentary: a pair of flippers for the feet, a diving mask and a utility knife.

"In case you're unfamiliar with the facts," he continued, "the flippers are used to give the diver greater propulsion. In fact, they transform him into a web-footed animal. The flippers are made of rubber and are patterned after the hind feet of a frog. The diving mask is merely a soft rubber water-tight mask into which is fitted a circular window of non-shatterable glass. It is used to give the diver better vision under water. The knife I carried was a serviceable hunting knife. Very sharp, it served as a defensive weapon as well as a tool to cut, pry or gouge specimens of algæ from the rocks or other substances to which they cling.

"Useful as they are, these aids do not enable the diver to stay under for prolonged periods. One can hold a full breath only for a limited number of seconds, then it becomes necessary to scuttle to the surface for a fresh air supply.

"For deeper and more protracted operations we had a so-called diving helmet, a cylindrical affair that fitted over the diver's head and rested on his shoulders. Air was supplied by a hose from a hand-operated air pump on the surface. In actual practice, however, it gave one a feeling of insecurity and a strange sense of claustrophobia. Indeed there were some who considered it dangerous. It was used rarely and only in shallow water.

"Of recent years sportsmen have adopted with some success the mask and flippers for underwater hunting. Armed with a spring gun capable of shooting dartlike projectiles or with a slender harpoon, they prowl at varying depths in search of their finny game. While it is a sport full of thrills, I would recommend it only for powerful swimmers in perfect physical condition. Several sad accidents have resulted from these 'skin divers' overtaxing their strength. The experienced diver never wastes his energy on the slightest unnecessary movement. The more daring and skilled skin divers have introduced a spirit of competition into the sport. They vie with one another in establishing depth records with the same fervor as pole-vaulters attempting to set a new height record.

"The champion of skin divers at this moment is Raimondo Bucher, an Italian flier, just turned forty. He made his record dive off Capri, not far from the famous Blue Grotto. He went down equipped only with goggles, flippers, web-fingered gloves and a nose-clip to equalize pressure on his eardrums. His only air supply was that which he carried in his lungs.

"The weather was bad, the water rough and cold. A weighted line was lowered from his boat to the bottom. Cork discs were attached to the line at intervals, each marked with the depth at which it was held.

"Bucher's first dive was a failure. Undaunted he tried again and reached a depth of 127.9 feet. Cork marker in hand, he

came to the surface in seventy-seven seconds, having attained
the greatest depth ever reached by a skin diver in a controlled
test. During the dive he was accompanied by a photographer
wearing an 'aqualung.' The feat was also recorded by a series
of remarkable photographs of Bucher at various phases of the
record-breaking dive."

"You have mentioned the aqualung as an aid to diving," I
said. "Will you describe it and how it functions?"

"With pleasure," he replied. But before he began I made
another request,

"Keep it simple, so I can understand what it is, what it does
and how it works."

My friend, the algæ hunter, nodded and with an understanding smile said, "I'll do my best!"

This is in substance what he told me.

A French naval officer who had spent almost all of his adult
life at sea, was an ardent swimmer. He had swum and dived
in all the Seven Seas but always as a blind man since underwater vision is blurred and limited.

In 1936 he acquired a pair of sea goggles that gave him sight
when swimming submerged. They also opened up a new empire of exploration rich in wonders hidden from humans since
the beginning of time. There was, however, one obstacle that
stood between him and discovery of the secrets of the unknown world that lay deep down under. Dependent on a
single full breath of air, the duration of his dives was limited
to seconds and the depth he could reach would rarely be more
than fifty or sixty feet. Determined to go deeper and stay
down longer, he began a series of experiments on an oxygen
rebreathing device. It was a failure from the start.

Then his thoughts turned to cylinders of compressed air
strapped to the diver's shoulders and piped to a mouthpiece
that would enable the diver to breathe. It looked good on

paper. In practice it failed because the contraption lacked an automatic valve that would feed the compressed air to the diver in ratio to his depth. He took his problem to an engineer who had perfected a valve to control the pressure of the natural gas used by automobiles in war-time France.

It took several weeks to design and construct a device in which the valve could be used. Tests in the Seine, a short distance from Paris, brought disappointment; the respirator functioned only when the wearer lay horizontally under water.

Back in the laboratory it was discovered that the failure was due to a slight error in design. This was corrected and another test dive made. Result: success far beyond expectation rewarded the inventors. Only then was the contrivance christened "Aqualung."

There was still more testing to be done. Hundreds of separate dives were made, each checked accurately for time and depth. A diver wearing goggles, fins and an aqualung remained submerged for an hour and swam down to a depth of 220 feet.

The French Navy was quick to see the possibilities of such an invaluable diving outfit and adopted the aqualung and immediately set about training a group of divers. These young men, all carefully selected for physical fitness and skill as swimmers, were taught and accustomed to the use of the aqualung in a depth of thirty feet. Classes were conducted, not only on land, but under water. In order to gain confidence the men were required while submerged to exchange their aqualungs. They were instructed also in the technique of conserving every ounce of energy by avoiding extreme exertion that would cause heavy breathing. Each movement of legs and torso must be slow and deliberate and made in such a manner as to appear almost listless. The arms of the divers were used only as an aid to balance and direction.

When these trained aqualungers had gained the required proficiency, they were assigned to the demolition of submerged explosives, relics of World War II that lay at the bottom of many French harbors. There was a sunken Nazi barge loaded with magnetic mines; also a disabled German submarine with its complement of torpedoes still intact. Most sinister of all was a field of KT mines so cunningly placed they could not be reached by mine sweepers. One by one these hazards were blown up and harbors made safe for shipping. Teams of four divers worked in half-hour shifts, each minute charged with danger.

When the job of demolition had been accomplished, the French Navy declared that it could not have been carried out by any other means. Conventional diving equipment—the ponderous, heavily weighted diving dress with its entangling air- and life-lines leading to the surface—would have so hampered the divers that catastrophe would have been inevitable.

And now the captain, co-inventor of the aqualung, sought fresh fields of usefulness. A new world of wonders awaited him undersea. There life in myriad forms, few of them known even to men of science, could be recorded and photographed and shown to the world.

He chose the Mediterranean as the scene of his operations. But first there was much to be done in the way of preparation: a suitable vessel to be fitted out; stores for a voyage of indefinite duration bought; scientific and diving equipment secured and tested; underwater photographic apparatus developed and built; and innumerable odds and ends acquired for the needs and comfort of the members of the expedition.

His chief problem concerned motion picture and still cameras. The aluminum housings with glass fronts in which they were encased were subjected to the same pressure as the divers who operated them. At 132 feet under they were subjected to a crushing pressure of 75 pounds to the square inch. Therefore the camera, like the diver who operated it, must be pressurized also.

In the Mediterranean, as in other waters, the diver is ever conscious of the shark menace. Members of the expedition who had encountered those "tigers of the sea," soon discovered that a spiked club was their best protection. A sharp rap on the snout of an approaching shark caused it to turn tail in rapid retreat.

Once while the captain and one of his cameramen were engaged in a sub-sea exploration at a depth of about fifty feet, they were startled by the sudden appearance of a large hungry-looking shark. It halted at close range as if to appraise its forthcoming meal. Instead of retreating the divers approached the creature cautiously—a tactic that had proved successful in many similar circumstances. When they were within a few feet of the intruder, two large blue sharks joined the party. The divers advanced zigzagging; the sharks retreated in like fashion. After about ten minutes of this maneuvering the photographer came close enough to one of the sharks to swing his twenty-one pound camera down on its head. For an instant there was a convulsive flailing of tails in a turmoil of swirling water as the trio of sharks vanished into the dim green haze.

While underwater cameras vary in design, all are built on the same principle. A conventional camera is secured within an aluminum housing with a glass front. It is both water-tight and air-tight. The controls for focus, diaphragm, shutter and film change are operated externally. But in spite of these precautions the cameras must have miniature aqualungs to equalize pressure, in order to avoid being crushed.

Typical is the Fenjohn underwater camera widely used by navies, scientific institutions, industrial concerns, yachtsmen and venturesome amateurs. It is made to withstand the high pressure of underwater work—shock, heat, sterilization and flying debris. On land it weighs twenty-one pounds but under water its weight is only three and three-quarters pounds.

The most important element in successful underwater or out-of-water photography is light of sufficient volume and of actinic quality to produce chemical changes in light-sensitive photographic emulsions.

To compensate for the fading of natural light as depth increased, flash-bulbs of 400,000 candle-power were the answer. But even they must be housed in pressurized reflectors lest they be crushed like eggshells.

In the dim and watery twilight deep down, all objects become a drab and dappled gray. Even the divers appear to each other as dusky silhouettes. Brightly hued fish are colorless except for a faint highlight along the dorsal area. But each flash-bulb burst into a momentary sphere of light, the divers found themselves for an instant in a riot of glowing color. Cliffs and caves, corals and ledges were encrusted with growths of dazzling reds, oranges, purples and greens, all blended in shades and tones and hues of weird beauty.

The deep does not give up its secrets, however, without striking back occasionally at those who venture too far into its domain. Below the 200-foot mark is dangerous territory that none but the most expert divers may invade. The violent increase in pressure charges the blood stream and body tissues with nitrogen that can be dissipated only by slow and tedious ascent with stops of varying duration at certain levels. Rapid ascent results in an attack of the "bends" or caisson disease, sometimes fatal and always accompanied by excruciating pain in the joints. Another threat to the diver below the danger line is a kind of intoxication. In its acute form the victim slips gradually from a state of exhilaration into a drunken stupor, then to unconsciousness and finally to death by drowning.

Such was the fate of one of the expedition's best divers. Having established a depth record of almost four hundred feet, he was carried away with the bravado of intoxication. Cutting out all caution, he tried to go still deeper. Soon losing consciousness, he joined "the legion of those who went down into the sea, never to return."

Since the introduction of "goggles" or diving masks and flippers as aids to underwater swimming, thousands of daring spirits have taken up underwater activities either as a sport or an outlet for their explorative urge.

One of the first to take up the new sport was the late Guy Gilpatric whom I knew for many years. He was a writer of note whose salty sea stories in the *Saturday Evening Post* and other magazines had endeared him to millions.

Desiring a change from the American scene, he took up residence in Nice, France, only a few miles from Monaco on the one side and Antibes on the other. The clear waters of the Mediterranean, rippling almost to his doorstep, beckoned. Heeding the call, he found a new and fascinating field of sport and exploration.

He reveled in the cool solitude he found deep in the limpid water bordering the shore. An accomplished swimmer, he loitered close to the bottom, peering into the nooks and crevices of rock and seaweed. His flippered feet moved with a gentle cadence, just enough to give him motion. The slender harpoon he carried was ever ready as he stalked an interesting specimen of fish. Occasionally an octopus, sprawling on a ledge, suddenly streamlined its tentacles and darted away in an inky cloud. Each day, and indeed each dive, revealed new wonders and brought new adventures.

At first his dives were of embarrassingly short duration, due in part to a limited lung capacity and in part to his unnecessary expenditure of energy. Several years of practice and an indomitable determination eventually gave him such control of breath and energy that he was able to stay under water for more than a minute, a time rarely exceeded even by pearl divers.

This faculty of controlling breath and energy does not seem to belong to any particular physical type. A star on the swimming team of one of our leading universities once confessed to me that if he were held under water for more than thirty seconds, he would drown. On the other hand the once famous diver and swimmer Annette Kellermann startled large theater audiences by her graceful underwater performances inside a glass tank and in full view of thousands. On many occasions she remained submerged for as long as two minutes.

Once while she was a week-end guest at our home I asked her how she had developed such amazing power both in and under water. The story she told me in answer to my question is worth repeating.

While she was a child in Sydney, Australia, Annette was stricken with polio. A prominent physician recommended swimming as a method of strengthening her afflicted muscles. Her mother, a retired opera star, employed a governess who was also a strong swimmer.

Then began a daily routine in which teacher and pupil went each morning to a nearby beach. At first the child was timid but soon she gained confidence. One day she swam a few struggling strokes. It was the turning point in her life, for while she was in the water her muscles co-ordinated, her crippled legs which could not support her on land, began to develop strength. Soon the water became her natural element. In it was freedom of movement and a semblance of normalcy. With the passing of the months came improvement in mind and body and an increased love of the water. When the governess returned to her native England, Annette then thirteen, continued her swimming and diving alone.

Now the Sydney beaches were noted for the number and size of sharks that infested them. Annette, now known as the "sea nymph," paid little heed to warnings of sharks. When she swam out to investigate, as she sometimes did, the savage creatures seemed to receive her as one of their kind. Anyway they never molested her.

By this time her fellow citizens began to take notice of this teen-ager's swimming and diving feats. Now she was strong of wind and limb; her entrance into the water brought applause from the beach loungers. One day a theatrical impresario was present. He was carried away by the skill and grace of this unknown girl. With an eye to business he sought her out and offered her an engagement at his theater in Sydney. He would construct a crystal-clear tank on the stage so thousands might watch her perform.

Flattered and flustered, Annette asked for time to think it over. She feared her mother's displeasure. Madame Kellermann, to increase the depleted family income, was giving music lessons to the young women of Sydney society.

Moved only by a desire to assist the family finances, Annette decided to accept the theatrical offer without her mother's knowledge.

A tank with a capacity of 8000 gallons was hurriedly built on the stage of the leading theater. A glass front and brilliant stage-lighting gave the audience a clear view of the interior.

On the fateful night when the curtain rose, Annette dressed in a black one-piece swimming suit, was seen poised on a high diving board in the blinding glare of a spotlight. The audience gasped. It was the first time, anywhere in the world that the one-piece suit had ever been worn by a girl in a public place. To the accompaniment of the orchestra and wild applause,

Annette Kellermann, a frightened and bashful teen-ager, made her theatrical debut with an exhibition of fancy diving and underwater ballet that held the audience spellbound.

Leaving the theater with the plaudits still ringing in her ears, Annette hurried home. She had decided not to break the good news to her mother until she could bring home her week's salary. Fate decided otherwise.

After breakfast the following day Madame Kellermann picked up the morning paper. Glancing at the front page, she gasped. There was terror in her eyes. For there in the headlines she saw her daughter's name followed by the story of her success in a vaudeville house.

Between sobs the mother explained to the bewildered child that her appearance on a vaudeville stage in her abbreviated swim suit meant the loss of the paying music pupils on whom they depended for their livelihood.

And so it did. At that time Sydney society was both snobbish and class conscious. That very day pupils scheduled for singing lessons failed to appear. Within a week it had become apparent that Madame Kellermann's music lessons were no longer welcomed in Sydney's exclusive circles.

Heartbroken at the grief she had caused her mother in all innocence, the girl determined to show the society snobs and sniffers that hard work and honest effort would bring reward.

Soon after her success in Sydney, Annette Kellermann's fame spread rapidly. Engagements were offered her in London, Paris, New York and other large cities. In a comparatively short time her annual earnings were far greater than those ever enjoyed by her mother as an opera star.

A strange commentary on the career of this ambitious girl is that her scanty swim suit, shocking as it was to Sydney society, became the rage all over the world. It was in fact the seedling from which has grown a great textile industry employing tens of thousands of skilled workers.

Before the Kellermann era swimming and diving, as practiced today, were all but unknown. A naked boy, holding his nose, leaped sprawling into the "ole swimmin' hole." His elders entered the water cautiously with splashings and splutterings. Women and girls wore "modest" skirts and bloomers, long black stockings and high-laced canvas shoes. A few yards with timid breast strokes marked the limit of their endurance. Few had witnessed the grace and poetry of dives from the "high board": the swan, the jackknife, the right and left twists and a variety of combinations.

As the Kellermann cult spread and swimming in all its forms became a national pastime, men, women and children took to the water like ducks. "Bathing" as it was called, became passé; "water sports" took its place.

Elaborate swimming pools became standard equipment in schools, clubs and luxury homes. In many student bodies the Australian crawl and back-stroke vied for favor with the forward pass and touchdown. Indeed some considered them as important in the curriculum as Latin or calculus. The Red Cross, always alert to public reactions, established swimming classes in numerous communities with safety and saving human lives their objectives. The Olympic Games added swimming and diving to the agenda. The thrilling experience of surf-boarding and water skiing was too enticing for many to resist. Several world's records are now held by young women whose forebears dared to defy the prudish Victorian edict that insisted all swimmers be swathed in cumbersome costumes.

Recent reports have it that much of the pearl-diving in the South Pacific now is done by native girls whose feats of endurance excel those of the native men who for centuries considered the undersea their undisputed domain.

Until quite recently water sports and activities were confined to the immediate vicinity of the surface. Rarely did divers from the highest springboard go more than a few feet under water. Exhibition dives from eighty-foot towers into tanks with a depth of six feet of water have been successfully made merely as a carnival entertainment.   U.S 1086365

The urge for exploration that has characterized the human race since its beginning may have spurred present-day adventurers to invade the mysterious and little-known territory that lies under the waters of the earth.

The introduction of the "swim-fin" or "flipper" opened new vistas for the swimmer by giving him increased propulsion, power of endurance and length of time he can stay submerged. The greater the energy expended in any sport or physical activity, the greater the strain on the lungs that must supply the life-giving oxygen.

Those who have seen a frog swim have observed the similarity of its motions to those of the human being doing a breast stroke. There the similarity ends, however. The frog moves swiftly and with graceful ease, getting its propulsion almost entirely from its web-footed hind legs. The human swimmer propels himself with a violent motion of arms and legs.

It was reasonable therefore that students of underwater swimming should profit from the lowly frog. After many attempts to simulate the little creature's webbed feet. flippers as we know them today, were perfected and adopted immediately by the devotees of undersea hunting and exploration. Made of rubber and ribbed for stiffness, they are worn on the feet like shoes. The huge flat soles take up the thrust of the swimmer's legs, giving him increased speed with reduced effort. On land the flippers give the wearers' legs a grotesque resemblance to those of a frog and so the demolition units of the United States Navy who adopted them for hazardous duties in action during World War II, were christened "Frog-men," now an honored nickname in our military services.

Having read hair-raising accounts of the Frogmen's heroism and listened to authentic epics of their daring in the face of almost certain death, I felt it to be my duty as a reporter to get the story of the Frogmen at first hand.

I was fortunate indeed to have as friend and neighbor Lieutenant Commander Joseph Gibbons who commanded several demolition units during the Normandy Invasion and who received in the name of his command a citation from Navy Secretary Forrestal for its outstanding gallantry on the now historic Omaha Beach.

"Tell me, Commander," I said, "just what are the duties of Frogmen?"

With the terseness of an official communique, he replied, "They are a technical and highly skilled force whose task is to clear invasion waters of enemy-built obstacles, so that landing craft and personnel can reach the beach with a minimum of loss."

"What were those wartime obstacles?"

"They varied," he explained. "Some were built of heavy steel beams, devilishly assembled in such a way that they presented barriers resembling huge bayonets ready to stab into the vitals of approaching vessels. They were completely submerged at high water of the twenty-one foot tide and so were invisible to landing craft headed for the beach. Others were ponderous gate-like barriers of steel intended to stop vessels dead in their tracks and so expose them to intensive fire from shore batteries. And then there were mines of many types. One of the most deadly was secured on top of a heavy timber set into the bottom at an angle of forty degrees and inclining toward oncoming craft. Complete destruction awaited the vessel that collided with one of them. Many other obstacles had cunningly concealed mines attached."

"How was the work of demolition carried on?" I inquired.

"The men were taken by landing craft to within four hundred yards of the shore marked for invasion. The swimmers were dropped off at planned intervals. They swam toward the beach, measuring the depth of the water, observing the character of the bottom and the type of obstacles in the water and on the shore. Usually this was done under heavy enemy fire. Their scouting finished, they swam back to the points at which they'd been dropped. By an ingenious rescue method developed for the purpose, the men were picked from the water without stopping the boat. This was done to evade small arms' fire on shore.

"Back in their respective vessels the men reported soundings and observations to an interrogation officer. From those reports charts and maps were made quickly for use by the Invasion Commander.

"The next step was the demolition of the obstacles that would hinder or endanger the landing crafts and their complements of invading troops. The Frogmen were briefed on the demolition operation and each assigned to the complete destruction of specific obstacles. Then with quantities of TNT and other explosives strapped to their chests, they made a return trip shoreward, during which they were dropped from the pick-up boat in locations where they had scouted previously.

"The swimmers placed the charges in the most vulnerable parts of the obstacles. Then when all the explosives were in position, properly fused and wired, the Frogmen, all but two, swam from the danger zone to be taken on board the pick-up boats. The two who remained waited for a smoke signal from one of the boats. On sighting it they pulled the fuse pins and swam in hasty retreat to join their team comrades. After an interval of a few minutes a series of explosions sent huge geysers of sea and sand skyward. Steel beams, chunks of concrete and metal fragments rained down on the churning water.

"In a matter of minutes after the Frogmen had accomplished their mission, phalanxes of landing craft came tearing in from seaward, passed safely over the shattered ruins of the deadly debris and grounded only a few yards from the water's edge. Ramps were lowered and fighting men by thousands in full battle equipment swarmed ashore, scarcely up to their armpits in water.

"That was typical of hundreds of landings made by our armed forces that could not have been accomplished but for the skill and daring of the Frogmen, officially known as UDTs —Underwater Demolition Teams.

"Whether on the Normandy beaches or the South Pacific island-to-island operations, the techniques, stamina and sheer heroism of the UDTs were the same. They were the same calibre of men who had received the same rigorous training and who were selected by the same standards—physical, mental and psychological."

Fascinated by Lieutenant Commander Gibbons' description of the Frogmen's combat activities, I asked, "Where and how are such supermen secured? How are they trained to carry on such hazardous work?"

I could see a flash of pride in the commander's eyes. "Remember," he said, "the service is entirely voluntary. It differs from other branches of the service in that height and weight specifications are not among the requirements.

"The Frogmen's first week of training, described as 'hell week,' familiarizes the men in what they may expect in the exacting business of demolition.

"Long and trying hours are spent in rubber boats, paddling against swift currents through cruel rocks. Tedious marches are made through swamps and thickets and rough terrain against planned attack with hand grenades. Damp hours are spent in foxholes with planted explosives, splattering mud and debris. All these season the men to conditions they will eventually meet. Swimming is of first importance. Before completing the ten-week course every man must prove himself able to swim a mile without fins and to be expert in underwater operations."

"Do many of the men pass such severe tests?"

"Not many," he replied. "From an original entry of one hundred twenty men, only thirty or forty graduate and receive their swim fins. The fins are a badge of honor indicating successful completion of the entire course."

"Is underwater demolition a new technique in warfare?" I inquired.

"No. It's as old as recorded history. For instance, the Athenians during the siege of Syracuse employed skilled divers to clear the harbor entrance of obstructions erected on the bottom to impede or prevent the passage of vessels. Alexander the Great, during his operations against Tyre, relied on a corps of trained divers to demolish undersea defenses built by the beleaguered city. Indeed in maritime warfare down through the ages underwater operations, whether in attack or defense, have played an obscure but important role."

"In the Second World War were casualties high among the Frogmen?"

A cloud passed over the officer's face. "Yes," he answered sadly, "sometimes as high as fifty percent."

"Were the obstacles demolished piecemeal or on a large scale?"

"Normally, high explosives were planted on a large group of obstacles. They were connected by lines of instantaneous explosive material. When the safety fuse was touched off, the whole area of obstacles went up together. On a prearranged signal, timed to a split second, all swimmers hastily retired from the area of danger to their pick-up boats and then to off-shore landing craft to escape the deluge of rock, concrete, steel and splintered timbers. Risks were tremendous. The Underwater Demolition Teams at Okinawa destroyed more than three thousand obstacles and nearly a third as many at Guam."

Despite my best efforts as a reporter I failed to draw from Lieutenant Commander Gibbons even a reference to his participation in the Omaha Beach operation. He was voluble, however, on the heroism of the men who worked beside and under him, also in praise of the Higher Command who conceived, developed and put into action the Frogmen.

Several days after my conversation with Lieutenant Commander Gibbons, I came across a clipping from the *Brooklyn Eagle*. It contained an interview with Seaman, 2nd Class, William Duffy aged seventeen, wearer of the Purple Heart who was just home from Normandy where he had served as a member of the demolition unit commanded by none other than my friend Lieutenant Commander Gibbons. Here in his own words is the boy's story:

"I was five hours on the Normandy Beach on D Day, crawling through sand in the first wave of battle. With sand in my eyes so I couldn't see and sand in my gun so I couldn't shoot, I lay there and prayed that I'd come through safely. I didn't.

"My unit, assigned to blast beach installations, preceded the infantry landings by three minutes. Many of us didn't make it to the beachhead.

"After five hours of crawling I 'got it' with shrapnel. I lay quiet awhile and then passed out. Later I found myself in a hospital near Bristol, England, where I remained for a month and a half.

"Those five hours I'll never forget. Above us were planes, thousands of them, swooping, bombing, strafing, fighting. Behind us were the land forces, mostly infantry. Everywhere was the awful noise of battle.

"In spite of fifty-three percent casualties, the one hundred seventy-one men of the unit cleared lanes for troop landings. That's about all."

3   **UNDERWATER HAZARD**

It was by mere chance I met Robert Davis, construction engineer, while we were passengers on an airliner from Montreal to New York. Soon we entered into conversation as air travelers frequently do.

In the course of our chat he casually mentioned an interesting project he was engaged on at the moment. A large power station in New York's upper East Side was installing a

42

new generator of tremendous capacity to replace four obso-
lete and less powerful dynamos that had given service for
nearly half a century.

He went on to mention that generators, or as they are sometimes called dynamos, are steam-driven and require vast quantities of water for the boilers and to cool and condense the
exhaust steam. The water was led in through tunnels so large
that an automobile could have been driven through any one
of them. Connected with the East River, the tunnels provided an inexhaustible supply of cooling water.

Since the new generator was located at a spot where the old
tunnels could not be used, the construction of new tunnels
and sealing off the old ones became necessary. This sealing
operation could be carried on only by a diver. And so the
workers on the job were treated to the strange sight of a deep-
sea diver at work within a building in the heart of Greater
New York.

I accepted an invitation from the construction engineer
and visited the power plant a few days later.

Within a cavernous room as large and high-ceilinged as a
modern theater I found a scene of furious activity. The fiery
hiss of cutting torches wielded by iron-masked men, the in-
cessant clang of hammers on steel, the thud of sledges on
concrete, the snorting of a huge crane lifting and swinging
great chunks of metal—all combined to make the place a
bedlam.

I was led to a roped-off area where the activity centered
around an open manhole from which protruded several feet
of a ladder. Close to the edge of the manhole a man stood
alert, his attention concentrated on the black hole at his feet.
He held a rope in one hand and a rubber air hose in the other.
Rope and hose led down into the opening. Nearby two men
operated an air-pump with the rhythm of a pendulum. It was

the source of the air supplied through the hose to the diver working under twelve feet of water. The faces of the men were serious. Conscious of having on their hands the life of a man, they paid little heed to what was going on around them.

For a moment I was puzzled about a second and heavier hose leading down into the manhole. Then I learned it came from a compressor supplying power to a compressed-air cutting tool which was being used by the diver to cut away certain sections of concrete in preparation for the construction of a bulkhead that would render one of the old tunnels inactive.

After looking on for ten minutes or so, I noticed the rope held by the "tender" on the edge of the manhole receive a sharp tug from below. It was a signal from the diver; he was coming up. The "tender" took in the lines as the diver ascended, coiling them fastidiously. Snarled lines are dangerous in an emergency.

Presently from the nether darkness rose the diver's helmet like a coppery bubble. It was followed by the ponderous metal breastplate, the belt of leaden weights and the cumbersome diving dress runneling water down over leaden-soled shoes.

As the diver stepped laboriously from the ladder to the concrete floor, the tender placed a rough stool for him to sit upon during his rest period.

In the surroundings of workaday activities the figure in copper, lead and rubberized armor looked for all the world like some invading monster from outer space. With the gentleness of a nurse removing a head bandage, the tender lifted the heavy helmet and lo! there was the kindly face of a man in his middle sixties.

Sweating and a little winded, he sat silent for a few minutes and then remarked, "It's a bit warmish down there." The water in which he had been working, coming from the steam-condensers, had the temperature of the steam room in a Turkish Bath.

When he had regained his breath, I asked him, "How does it feel to work down in the vitals of a great city?"

"Nothing to it," he replied. "Once you go under, what's over you makes no difference as long as you get plenty of air." And then he went on, "My last job was in a flooded mine nearly a thousand feet down. It was a pump repair job in only fifteen feet of water. The whole thing took less than three hours but the water was so cold I nearly froze to death. In this business there's no telling what the next job will be. Last summer I was called to a smart yacht club on Long Island. One of the country's wealthiest women and owner of a large yacht had lost a valuable bracelet overside while boarding the ship's launch.

"Swinging at a mooring in a strong ebb tide, the yacht had changed position many times before I came on board. The bracelet might be anywhere on an acre of muddy bottom. The day was bright and the water smooth and warm. Just as my tender was about to screw on my helmet, one of the men on the airpump remarked, 'Looks to me like hunting a needle in a haystack.' And I must admit I felt the same way.

"As I went over the side, I remembered it was Friday, my lucky day, but when I hit the bottom, I lost faith in Lady Luck. The mud, while not deep, was soft as porridge. Any small object falling on it would be swallowed up. However, I went on with the search.

"When I had gone about fifty feet from the ship, I saw just a few feet ahead of me a tiny speck of light glinting off some bright object. I moved cautiously so as not to stir up the mud. I investigated and, believe it or not, there on an old eel-pot, half buried in the mud, was the lost bracelet, laid out its full length as if a maid had placed it carefully on a dressing table.

"As I was about to leave the yacht, a steward told me the owner would like to see me on the after deck. And so, as I came aft, she rose to greet me with tears of thanks. The bracelet, she said, was not of great value, but it was priceless as a family heirloom. It had been presented to her grandmother by one of Europe's crowned heads."

When he had finished his breather and given certain instructions to his tender, the diver had his helmet again screwed to his breastplate. Lumbering to the manhole, he gave me a friendly wave of his hand and disappeared slowly into the darkness below.

A few days later Davis, the engineer, was my luncheon guest at the Dutch Treat Club. Among its members are high-ranking men in letters, music, art and science. After a pleasant and informative hour-and-a-half we sought a quiet corner where we could chat without interruption. I was fairly bursting with questions. I wanted to ask about commercial diving and more particularly, commercial divers—their background, their equipment, their work and their hazards. It was an easy interview. My guest had a startling facility for words, a keen perception of human interest and an encyclopedic knowledge of the subject.

We chatted late into the afternoon. When he had left, I leafed through my notes and was astonished at the amount of information I had secured, bit by bit. It is from those notes I tell in substance the engineer's story:

Of all modern trades, skills, professions or callings that have an important bearing on our daily lives, the diver and his work is the least known to the public at large. For example, during the Worlds Fair held at Flushing Meadow, New York City, in 1939, millions of people from all over the world assembled around the famous lagoon to witness a spectacle of breath-taking beauty. Each night at an appointed hour a forest of geysers rose majestically from the mirrorlike water to prance and gambol and curtsey like ballet dancers in a billion candle-power flood of light impregnated with all the colors of the rainbow. The "oohs!" and "ahs!" of the spectators were an index of their mystification and enjoyment. Not one in a million knew that a diver was on nightly patrol in the intricate network of pipes and valves that lay under the surface of the lagoon.

Unlike other skilled workers, the commercial diver must be a jack-of-all-trades. He never knows from one job to another what his next assignment will be. It may be one of inspection of some underwater structure having to do with a bridge, a pier, a factory on the water's edge. Or it may be a salvage operation on a sunken vessel.

Skilled divers are employed extensively by the Navy, the Coast Guard, the Army Engineers, Salvage and Construction Companies, Municipal Water Companies, in off-shore oil operations and indeed in all industries and activities where manual work must be carried on under water.

Although professional diving is considered a hazardous occupation, accidents, particularly fatal ones, are rare. This can be attributed first to the mental and physical calibre of the men. They are a sober, steady and resourceful lot to whom "nerves" are unknown and who never take a chance if the odds are against them. They consider unnecessary danger not as something to be faced but to be avoided. Secondly, wherever divers are employed, elaborate precautions are taken for their safety. Chief in importance is the air supply. On some salvage vessels the life-giving air comes from a power-driven air-compressor, but more often it is supplied by a hand-operated air-pump activated by two men. The key man in the diver's retinue is the tender; on his shoulders alone rests the safety and the working ease of his charge. It is he who personally attends to the almost sacred rite of dressing the diver in his two-hundred-pound armor. It is a ceremony of infinite detail.

On a low stool sits the diver, wearing two suits of thick woolen underwear, a heavy sweater, several pairs of woolen stockings and a knitted watch cap. He sits stoically as a monarch during a ceremonial robing. His diving dress of rubberized canvas, resembling a gargantuan infant's sleeping suit, is drawn up over legs and torso to chest height. His arms go into the sleeves and his hands are forced through the soft rubber cuffs that fit the wrists so tightly that water cannot enter. The top of the dress is then pulled up to the shoulders.

Next in order comes the forty-pound metal breastplate. It rests on the diver's shoulders, covering the upper part of his chest and back. The upper edge or hem of the diving dress is gripped by a double flange on the breastplate and secured by a series of wing nuts, thus making the union of metal and fabric both water-tight and air-tight.

A pair of ponderous boots are now put on the diver's feet. They are made of sturdy leather; the soles are heavy slabs of lead to which are fastened strong metal toe-caps to protect the wearer's feet from injury by falling objects. Laces of stout cord are supplemented by three leather straps buckled tightly over the insteps. The boots weigh about forty pounds.

Neatly coiled nearby the diver's "lines" are in readiness. The lifeline, secured around the diver's body, has two functions: first, it is a means of lowering or raising the bulky figure and secondly, it is a means of communication between diver and tender. Signals are passed from one to the other in a code of sharp tugs on the lifeline.

In some operations communications to and from the bottom are carried on by telephone; this, however, means another line and an increased risk of fouling—one of the major hazards of workers under water.

Now dressed from the neck down, the diver awaits the placing of the helmet or "hat" as it is sometimes called. It is the crowning moment of the dressing ritual. Almost as large as a ten-gallon iron pot and as heavy, the helmet is lowered gently over the diver's head and screwed with a quarter turn onto the breastplate. The air-line is coupled to it immediately and the tender signals for air so that the inmate, encased in his heavy armor, can breathe.

With the first whiff of welcome air the diver rises and lumbers slowly toward a ladder leading into the water. Before he descends, however, there is still a finishing touch to be added. An eighty-pound girdle of leaden weights is placed around his waist. It is suspended from his shoulders with stout leather straps. Then after a last-minute check to make sure everything is in order, the tender raps on the diver's helmet the signal meaning "Okay. Let's go!"

Clumsily and with great deliberation the man-in-armor goes down the ladder. As the water closes down over his helmet, he gently heaves himself backward and is on his way to the bottom.

When the water is comparatively shallow and the work light, the diving helmet is a simple affair. It is just large enough for the diver to turn his head inside it in order to see through the shatterproof glass windows placed in front and on each side. The glass is protected by a metal grill so designed that it does not impair vision. The air-line is coupled to the back of the helmet while in front and to the right is a valve to be used to control the flow of outgoing air.

This valve has several uses. Besides controlling the breathing air within the diving dress, it can be used to give the diver a certain amount of buoyancy. When the valve is closed down until the outgoing air is less than the incoming air, the diver's dress becomes inflated, thus displacing a certain weight of water; this makes the diver and his heavy outfit slightly lighter than the surrounding water. The resultant buoyancy enables him to make prodigious leaps in slow motion over obstacles or to soar from the sea bottom to the deck of a sunken ship.

In a grave emergency it is possible for the diver to inflate his air-tight dress until he resembles a bloated monster and so pop to the surface, a grotesque human bubble. But that is a dangerous practice, since it almost always brings on an attack of the dreaded "bends," or caisson disease.

When the human body is subjected to great air pressure for a period, whether it be in deep water, a tunnel or a caisson, the blood and tissue become impregnated with nitrogen. A sudden change to normal atmospheric conditions causes the gas to form a froth of tiny bubbles that course through the circulatory system. The victim suffers intense pain, particularly in the joints. Crippling and sometimes death follow. There seems to be only one remedy for the disease—slow decompression.

The victim is placed in a metal cylinder known as a "decompression chamber," into which air is pumped at a pressure equal to that in which the victim was at work. Then the pressure is reduced gradually, very slowly, to that of the surrounding air.

Slow decompression while rising to the surface is a most important part of the diver's routine. While being raised from the bottom, he is halted at intervals and left dangling like a spider on the end of a web. The halting periods vary with the depth from which he is being raised. His ascent, after a deep dive, may take two or more hours, a tedious experience requiring a world of patience.

If a decompression chamber is not available on the job and

a diver is threatened with the bends, a reasonably effective treatment may be substituted by putting the diver back in his diving dress and helmet, then binding arms, legs and torso round and round with a light rope. After this, air pressure is applied until it approximates the pressure under which the diver worked. The rope binding is necessary to keep the inflated diving dress from bursting.

The name "bends," as applied to caisson disease, has a curious origin. Many years ago, before the development of the modern diving dress, underwater construction was done in caissons which were huge wooden structures resting on the bottom and kept under air pressure to exclude the water.

At that time a member of the Greek royal family who was world famous as an arbiter of fashion, became slightly deformed as a result of a physical condition. To conceal her deformity she assumed a bent-forward posture and walked with a mincing step. Fashionable women the world over were quick to adopt not only the styles worn by the Grecian noblewoman but to imitate her bent posture. The fad was promptly christened the "Grecian Bend."

In those days caisson disease was prevalent among workers in compressed air. Since modern decompression methods were practically unknown, many of the victims who escaped death were left with a permanent stoop that resembled the Grecian Bend. And so in time the disease itself became known as "the bends."

The commercial diver is among the highest paid of all skilled labor. In many cases he is self-employed, that is, his services are available whenever or wherever they are needed. Often he is employed permanently by construction or salvage companies who regard him as a skilled technician capable of carrying on underwater arduous tasks planned by engineers and salvage experts. On occasion his services are required by police and other law enforcement officers. Many a criminal has been brought to justice through the efforts of a diver who has recovered the lethal weapon, the loot or even the corpse so important as evidence in a court of law.

I remember well a sweltering summer day when I was taken in a New York police car to the scene of a crime, there to watch a diver at work. It was during a trucking strike distinguished by bitterness and hatred on both sides. One night a motor truck, parked on the waterfront, was driven over the stringpiece and into the East River where the tides run as swiftly as seven miles an hour. On receiving the report of the sabotage the Harbor Police took over.

Arriving on the scene, I saw two police boats grappling unsuccessfully for the submerged truck. A diver accustomed to police work was called in. I watched him go down into thirty feet of murky water and followed his air bubbles on the surface as he prowled along the bottom.

At first it appeared a simple job. Tire marks clearly showed where the vehicle was driven into the river. Hours passed, however, without the discovery of the truck. With approaching darkness the search was abandoned for the night.

The following morning I returned to the scene. The diver was at work several hundred feet downstream from where he had begun the search. About noon the tender felt three sharp pulls on the lifeline—the signal that the diver wished to be hauled up—he had found the errant truck. During its twenty hours in the river it had been swept along the bottom for a distance of nearly three hundred feet from the spot where it entered the water.

Where the tides run so swiftly, the diver can work only during the period of high or low water when the current slackens its pace. Those who are experienced in bottom fishing with a light sinker know that in swift water bait and sinker are swept to the surface. That is precisely what happens to the diver in a strong current. Although he can *decrease* his weight by inflating his diving dress, he is powerless to *increase* it so as to hold himself on the bottom.

That is only one of the multitude of elementary facts the diver must store up during his apprenticeship. Formerly he learned his trade the hard way, picking up odds and ends of useful information while assisting in readying an experienced diver—lowering him, raising him, understanding and obeying his signals, noting at times the wiles and treacheries of explosives, familiarizing himself at odd moments with the tools of the trade—crowbar and cutting torch, shovel and sledge hammer, ship carpentry, concrete- and ironwork. He was lucky if some old hand at diving took a liking to him and gave him sage advice and practical instruction.

Today the diver-to-be goes to school. He learns the fundamentals and fine points of his chosen profession under able and experienced instructors. His classroom may boast a blackboard or it may be under water. In either case he knows that his future depends on his ability to absorb instruction and to apply what he learns to the exacting tests to which he will be subjected.

Diving is no longer a job. It is a highly skilled profession that calls for many attributes which only a few possess—physical endurance, highly developed intelligence and an intuitive rather than an academic knowledge of engineering. Men possessing those characteristics are scarce. It was not until World War II that the scarcity of expert divers became a national problem.

When the French ocean liner *Normandie* was sunk on February 9, 1942, at her pier in New York harbor, the United States Navy was confronted with a salvage job of overwhelming proportions. Forty thousand tons of dead weight, the doomed vessel lay on her side on the muddy bottom with half of her huge bulk out of water. Gutted by fire and helpless as a dead whale, the onetime luxurious liner presented a challenge to the best brains in the business of marine salvage.

The Navy with limited experience in raising sunken vessels called on the Merritt, Chapman & Scott Corporation, whose name in the field of marine salvage is known all over the world.

Since a huge amount of underwater work had to be done, outside as well as inside the stricken ship, it was evident that a large number of divers would have to be secured. Skilled divers, however, were rare since they were frequently employed in enterprises vital to the war effort. A countrywide search failed to produce more than a handful of men of the required calibre.

For a while it looked like a stalemate. Then the Navy and the Salvage Company devised a daring plan: they would establish a diving school at the scene of the foundered vessel; the curriculum would include instruction in every essential phase of the diver's profession from reading blueprints to the proper handling of the blue-flamed cutting torch. In a short time the enrollment numbered a hundred students, every one of them picked with the utmost care for their physical, psychological and intellectual characteristics.

Whether the diving school would prove a success was anyone's guess during its early days. Presently a surprise awaited the founders. The student divers, throwing themselves wholeheartedly into their exacting studies, showed unusual aptitude in the varied skills needed in their professional work. In diving dress they carried on like veterans, executing their underwater tasks in a manner highly satisfactory to their superiors. Today many of those men are among the most highly skilled divers in the United States if not in the world.

With the *Normandie* raised and again on an even keel the Navy continued its diving school along the most advanced lines. The experiences gained in the herculean task of raising and righting the big ship were invaluable in the development of new techniques and equipment.

Because of his special training, the hazards of his job and the unusual precautions taken for his safety, the Navy diver is looked upon as a man of distinction. Indeed there are some who call him the prima donna of the underwater service.

Unlike the commercial diver who is frequently something of an individualist, the Navy man works under the strictest supervision. His physical condition is watched as carefully as if he were a star athlete. He eats, sleeps, exercises and lives according to any unyielding schedule. His dives and ascents and rest periods are on order. When he is brought up from great depths, his ascent is timed scientifically to insure him against the bends. If for some unforeseen reason he should become exposed to an attack of the disease there is a decompression chamber and skilled operators awaiting him.

The hazards of a particular job are carefully studied and instruction given him on how to avoid them or in case of emergency how to overcome them.

The commercial diver on the other hand is on his own once he goes under. Capable though he be, he is sometimes confronted by an unexpected condition or situation of which competent engineering could advise or warn him. Such a case happened a few years ago when a diver was trapped under water because he failed to consider certain physical laws which would be familiar to any competent engineer. A gate valve controlling the outflow of a municipal water reservoir became jammed while in a wide-open position. Every effort to close it failed while millions of gallons of precious water were being wasted.

It was evident that repairs could not be made until the water, rushing through the intake pipe, was shut off. After hours of discussion by officials it was decided that the only practical method of shutting off the inflow through the thirty-inch intake pipe would be to place a weighted wooden ball or sphere over the opening through which the precious water was stampeding.

Of course a diver would be necessary to guide the wooden ball into place. It seemed on paper to be a comparatively simple operation and so a free-lance diver who owned his own equipment, was employed. He was widely known by the appropriate name of Davey Jones.

Early the next morning Davey, his crew and his equipment arrived on the dam that held back billions of gallons of water. A number of spectators had come to witness the strange rite of a man at work under water.

Dressed in his heavy armor, the diver lumbered to the ladder that led down to the bottom of the reservoir and soon disappeared under the surface. The wooden ball, cored with lead to overcome its buoyancy, was lowered into the water a little to the north side of the intake.

Since the sphere had practically no weight when submerged, Davey handled it with ease as he moved it cautiously toward the opening through which the water was rushing. Soon he felt a gentle current that increased as he inched forward to a position where he could put the ball in place.

Suddenly the sphere was almost wrenched from his grip. As he struggled to hold on to it, he was swept from his feet and flung bodily toward the opening, the ball slightly in the lead. Before he could attempt to escape the maelstrom, he crashed violently against the retaining wall at a point close to the opening. Half stunned, he felt a sharp pain shoot up his left leg.

Recovering his full senses, he was glad to see that the ball was in place but he also realized that his left ankle was caught between the ball and the metal edge of the opening. Middle-aged but still physically powerful, he strove with all his strength to extricate his foot. All effort was futile. He knew then he was trapped.

Signaling his tender to pull him free with the lifeline, he braced himself for the torture he knew would follow. However, even with several men on the rope, the ball and water refused to break their grip.

Word went out that a diver had been trapped in the reservoir. Crowds flocked to the scene. Officials hurried from their offices. Rescue plans were formulated and abandoned. None knew what had happened to the diver. They only knew he was alive and strong as indicated by his lusty pulls on the lifeline. That his air supply was ample, was evidenced by the rising froth of bubbles.

Ultimately it was decided to employ another diver to go down to release the imprisoned man. Hours later a diver arrived from New York. In the meantime the endangered man had grown weaker, the tugs on his lifeline were scarcely perceptable. At one point they ceased but were renewed after an interminable quarter hour when he gave no reply to the signals of his tender.

On arrival the rescue diver was briefed on the situation. His crew whom he had brought with him, set up his air-pump and laid out the various items of his diving dress. His tender carried out the ritual of dressing him. His helmet, a large and roomy affair, was of a type much used by the Navy. It differed from the everyday diving helmet in that it had an extra window near the top, so that by throwing back his head he could look upward. A telephone, an integral part of the helmet, was connected with a head-phone used by his tender.

A spark of hope kindled in the breasts of workers and by-standers as the water closed over the rescue diver. Only *he* could save a life that was slowly ebbing. On reaching the victim he pressed his helmet against that of the trapped man and shouted, "Are you okay?" A faint voice whispered weakly, "Okay." This device is often used by divers to communicate with each other when working under water. The tender, listening intently in his ear-phones, relayed the diver's message, "Alive but weak."

The rescue diver also reported that the trapped man's ankle and heavy boot, caught between the ball and the edge of the pipe, had made a crescent-shaped opening that permitted water to flow through with terrific force but in greatly reduced volume. The ball was held immovable by the tremendous water pressure behind it. The pipe, embedded in an inset in the heavy masonry, gave no opportunity for inserting a pry bar for leverage that would dislodge it enough to release the victim.

Seven hours had passed since it was discovered the diver had been trapped. Night was approaching. Powerful lights flooded the bleak stage where tragedy was being enacted. Occasional faint tugs on his lifeline told that Davey Jones was still alive.

With the flow of water reduced, work on the disabled gate valve was carried on at a furious pace. The rescue diver went down again and again merely to give an encouraging pat on the shoulder of his charge or to shout an enlivening word through touching helmets.

It was almost daybreak when it was announced that the stubborn gate valve was ready for operation. Before it was closed, the visiting diver went down to stand by for the release of the man who now appeared to be unconscious if not actually dead. He phoned his tender, "Okay. Shut 'er off!"

With the outlet now closed the inward rush of water slackened and in a few minutes ceased. When the huge pipe was filled to capacity, the imprisoning ball, relieved of the pressure of the impounded water, rose slowly to the surface.

The limp form of Davey Jones was hoisted gently upward. After his helmet and heavy trappings had been removed, he regained consciousnes and was hurried away to a hospital. Slim, the faithful tender, looked at his watch, and exclaimed, "Eighteen hours under water—and still alive. Davey's tough and no mistake!"

When questioned by reporters a few days later, Davey Jones could see nothing in his adventure that would interest the reading public.

"That's the chance you take," he said between puffs on his pipe, "and nobody forces you to take it."

4   MIRACLE WORKERS

About the middle of the last century, long before radio, radar, loran and other electronic aids to navigation were heard of, ship sinkings from various causes were an everyday occurrence. Reports of vessels "lost without trace" were published with tragic frequency. Some met their end and oblivion in the far and lonely reaches of the oceans. Others suffered disaster nearer the shore and in shallower water where daring men could reach them in the then new-fangled "closed" diving dress. Soon a profitable but hazardous business sprang up. Cargo, valuables and often the ship itself were saved to the owners or to the insurance underwriters.

Those were the days of the windjammers when American sailing ships were supreme on the seven seas. Hard-bitten shipmasters and bucko mates drove their vessels to break a record, to beat a rival or win a wager. Caution and seamanship were often cast to the winds. As a result the beaches and shoals along the Atlantic coast were literally dotted with the wrecks of once proud ships.

In 1860, Captain Israel J. Merritt, a young and stalwart man who had made a name for himself as a "wrecker," established the Merritt Wrecking Company. Success followed. The business grew in stature and maritime importance.

Meanwhile W. L. Chapman, energetic and resourceful in his work, established himself in the salvage and other fields as an authority on lifting great weights from both sea and land by means of derricks. His firm was widely known as the Chapman Derrick Company.

In 1897 the two companies pooled their resources and formed the Merritt Chapman Derrick and Wrecking Company. It was a name that in the decades to come grew famous in shipping circles all over the world. Hard work, mental and physical, coupled with an intuitive knowledge of the sea and its treacheries, brought success. Expansion followed. Construction was added to the company's activities. Eventually the map of the world was peppered with dots that showed the locations of Merritt Chapman operations that had been successfully completed or of projects in progress. A fleet of salvage vessels, equipped and manned to handle a salvage job anywhere, hurried like ambulances to scenes of marine disaster.

Indicative of the spirit that spurred the young organization to supreme effort was the stock question of one of its founders, W. L. Chapman, who invariably asked on the completion of a difficult operation, *"Did you do a good job?"*

In all industry there is none that presents as many knotty problems as marine salvage. Conditions vary so widely, no two jobs are alike. Each operation is a challenge to the inventiveness, skill and daring of the salvage crew.

The behavior of wind and sea, tides and currents, often determines the magnitude of the task. A vessel lying on the bottom in, say, a hundred feet of water, is hidden from view as completely as if it were a thousand fathoms under. There is no device that will enable the salvors to appraise the damage or plan the salvage operation. Only the diver can survey the wreck and secure the necessary data. In most salvage work he is the indispensable man.

Although commercial diving has been practiced in one way or another for centuries, it was a primitive and dangerous calling. The air supply carried in the diver's lungs was adequate for a stay under water of only a minute or two. Heavy work as performed by the modern diver was impossible. Depths rarely exceeded thirty feet.

It was not until 1788 that an engineer named Smeaton developed the diving bell that enabled men to work under water for hours at a time. It was based on a simple principle of physics: the air in an empty vessel immersed in water with the mouth down, will prevent water from entering except in a very small quantity.

Smeaton's diving bell was an inverted vessel weighing seven tons. Rectangular in shape, it resembled a giant cowbell. A narrow platform or seat accommodated two workers who got their air supply through a hose leading to an airpump on the surface.

Because it enabled men to work under water for comparatively long periods, the diving bell was welcomed by engineers and others concerned with salvage. It had its limitations, however. Men could work only on whatever was immediately beneath the opening. Many simple jobs that would be routine to the modern diver could not be done. Primitive and inefficient as it was, it sharpened the wits of inventors.

It was not until 1829 that an engineer named Siebe developed a diving dress that gave the wearer considerable mobility. A forerunner of present-day diver's armor, it consisted of a helmet attached to a waterproof, hip-length jacket. The air supply, pumped into the helmet, was allowed to escape below the jacket. Hence it was called an "open dress." At first it seemed to be the solution to the problem of carrying on work under water. In actual use, however, it proved something of a failure when it was discovered the wearer could work only in an upright position. When he stooped over, his supply of air escaped quickly under the hem of the garment.

Discouraged but undaunted, Siebe set about devising a complete suit of diving armor that would exclude water and retain controlled air pressure. It was more of a task than he had reckoned, for it was twenty-eight years later, in 1857, when he gave the world the "close dress" that was in all its essentials as we know it today. It gave the diver freedom of movement during many engineering and salvage operations. Without it such projects would have been dangerously difficult if not totally impossible.

Since Siebe's day many improvements have been introduced in the diver's equipment. Sturdier materials, better design and manufacture, advances in scientific knowledge have all contributed to the efficiency and safety of these men who work in the dim twilight of the bottom or the stygian blackness of a ship's interior.

The foreman of a salvage job on which two divers were at work, said to me, "To my knowledge, there is no trade or profession or calling that demands so many qualifications as that of the commercial diver. He must be physically sound and mentally balanced. He must have inventiveness, resourcefulness, plus unusual skill in the use of the tools and implements of many trades. His integrity must be as flawless as that of a surgeon, for on his diagnosis of conditions he finds under water is based the course and technique of a salvage operation or the success of an underwater construction project.

"Although he may deny it, I am convinced that somewhere in his make-up there is also just a dash of boyish love of adventure. I say that because the diver, more than any other worker I know, loves his job, its thrills, its challenges and the fantastic twilight world in which he works."

It was with the aid of such staunch and stalwart men that the firm of Merritt Chapman laid the foundation of their success in the field of salvage, and subsequently in the field of construction.

As the years passed and new skills and new equipment were developed, the salvage business assumed an aspect undreamed of in its earlier days. Indeed the work of the firm took on an amphibious character since many of its operations were on land as well as in water.

The business now had attained such proportions it had become necessary to reorganize it along more modern lines. And so came into being the firm of Merritt Chapman & Scott Corporation. Thomas A. Scott, a man of wide experience, vision and unusual executive ability, like his fellow members believed the impossible to be but a little more difficult. Marine construction was in his blood, for his father's name, Captain Thomas A. Scott, will stand high in the roster of men who fought the sea and won. It was he who carried on a seven-year battle to wrest a small patch of bottom from the Atlantic and on it to erect a lighthouse that will live through the ages. As a saga of man against a relentless sea, Captain Tom Scott's herculean task is well worth the telling:

From the earliest days of our country Race Rock, a submerged glacial boulder, near the entrance to Long Island Sound, was the terror of seafarers. Situated off Ram Island, it was swept by treacherous currents, battered by easterly storms, smothered in buttermilk fogs and hidden in winter by extensive ice-fields that drifted over it. In a period of a few years in the early nineteenth century more than a score of vessels piled up on the Rock with tragic loss of life and property.

A shocked Congress appropriated funds to erect a navigational light on the danger spot. The planning and construction of Race Rock Light were entrusted to a young man who even then had a wide reputation as artist and writer but whose ability as a construction engineer was known to only a few. His name: F. Hopkinson Smith.

With complete confidence in his own ability, Smith accepted the commission. There was but one problem that had him baffled—where to secure a foreman on whom he could depend in the emergencies that were sure to arise. Then one morning, as if fate had ordained it, a broad-shouldered cleancut man with an honest face entered his office. "I'm Captain Thomas Scott," the stranger said.

Smith knew at once he had found his man, for he had heard many times of Tom Scott's exploits as a diver and of his irresistible drive in getting difficult work done. And so began a union of two spirits—one the practical dreamer, the other the practical man-of-action.

Preparatory work was begun without delay. An elliptical

island of heavy rocks was built around and over the murderous boulder. Carried to the scene at Race Rock on schooners and scows, thousands of rocks, each weighing from three to seven tons, were piled into position. After a year of killing work they rose above the water at low tide. During that period Captain Scott spent almost as much time under water as he did out of it. His disregard for fatigue or danger was a challenge to the men who worked under his supervision.

All that could be shown for a year's hard labor was a confusion of jagged rocks, kelp-covered and slimy. Before actual building could begin the projecting rocks must be shaved down by blasting to a level surface as large as a tennis court.

New and unexpected problems arose. When the blasts were ready to be set off, the men took to the boats and rowed out of the area of flying rock fragments. This was practical only during the short period of slack water. When the swift tide was running full, it took an hour or two of strenuous rowing for the men to return to their work.

To save time and toil, the resourceful Captain Scott blasted out a kind of foxhole among the boulders and covered it with heavey timbers as a protection for his men. Here they crouched, sometimes up to their chins in water, while charges detonated all around them.

Captain Scott and his crew lived on the schooner *Wallace*, moored seaward at a safe distance. One evening when there was not even a suggestion of danger and Scott and his men were resting or sleeping, two hundred pounds of blasting powder in the schooner's hold exploded from some unknown cause. A number were killed; the others, including Captain Scott, were seriously injured. As Scott, stunned and bleeding, came to the surface, his foghorn voice bellowed to the rescuers, "See after those men first!"

Burned and bruised, he spent several weeks in an improvised

hospital. Meanwhile work had stopped. Clean sea air, rugged nursing and the will to win eventually got the men back on their feet. Work was resumed, but gales, fog, ice and storm-driven tides caused many delays.

Each day brought unexpected crises. Once a sloop, loaded with stone, was caught in the murderous eddies and swept plunging toward the rock foundation. Scott, dressed in his diving suit, saw tragedy in the making. Entering the water up to his arm-pits, he awaited the oncoming sloop with arms outstretched, as if preparing to wrestle. Lifted on a swell, the vessel came within arm's length. Placing his broad shoulders against the bow, Scott gave a mighty heave and the sloop missed a submerged rock by inches. This was repeated again and again while men made fast a line on the vessel's stern and carried it to a spar-buoy moored a hundred feet out. The line was passed through a snatch block and returned to the rocky pile where a puffing hoisting engine pulled the sloop back to safety. Scott called for his diving helmet and continued his work under water.

During the building of that rock foundation Scott was known to spend as long as seven continuous hours under water—a feat rarely equaled except through accident or in an emergency.

After nearly seven years of toil and heartbreak Race Rock Light was completed. It stands today defiant of the elements, a monument to the spirit of a man who defied defeat.

Thomas A. Scott, master diver, salvage expert without equal in difficult underwater construction, was a true American type. With little formal schooling, he went to work at an early age. When scarcely out of his teens, he undertook salvage jobs that had baffled older heads.

While employed by a New York salvage company, he was put in charge of the demolition of a sunken steamer that menaced navigation. Several other concerns had attempted to break up the iron hulk and failed. In diving dress Scott crawled over every foot of the vessel above and below deck, planning his attack as he went. With plans perfected he went ashore and purchased thirty wine casks, each with a sixty-gallon capacity. When the casks arrived on board the salvage vessel, each was filled to the brim with black powder and sealed. Modern high explosives were then unknown.

Days of hazardous toil followed as young Scott in clumsy diving dress sank each cask and maneuvered it to some vital spot in the wreck. Some he placed under her lower deck, others close to the boilers. Several were set in the forecastle and wherever the explosive force would have greatest effect. All the powder casks were connected by rubber-covered wires that in turn were twisted into an improvised cable that led to an electric battery on board the salvage ship where, at a safe distance, he was to set off the blast.

When everything was in readiness, he threw the switch. An acre of water and smoke and shattered metal shot hundreds of feet into the air. The roar could be heard for miles.

During his lifetime as one daring exploit came close on the heels of another, Captain Scott acquired the respect and love of all who knew him. In a brief essay on the master diver F. Hopkinson Smith wrote, "He was a man who was not afraid and who spoke the truth."

Occasionally a project without precedent comes along. It is a challenge. New principles, new techniques, new methods must be discovered or devised before the work can be begun. At first it seems to be beyond the bounds of possibility; then it slowly assumes a feasible aspect; later it emerges from impossibility and becomes another difficult job to be done and done without flaw.

Just such a burden was laid squarely on the shoulders of the Merritt Chapman & Scott Corporation and the Corbetta Construction Company when they secured a joint contract to build the substructure and deck of a concrete pier nearly four city blocks long and as wide as the average Main Street. The catch was that the huge structure must float and be navigable as a canoe.

The event leading up to this assignment occurred in 1947. A destructive fire demolished New York's ancient pier 57, then occupied by the Grace Steamship Lines. Beneath the twisted wreckage were the charred tops of some 3000 timber piles that had supported the old structure. These had to be cut off, one by one, close to the bottom, by a corps of divers employed by another contractor. To remove each pile in its entirety would have been both costly and time-consuming. To make matters more difficult, the river bottom at the pier site was semi-liquid silt incapable of bearing the load that must be placed upon it.

And so it was decided to build a pier that would be a huge pontoon with 90 percent of its dead weight supported by its own buoyancy. The plans called for the construction of three re-enforced concrete "boxes," two of which were to be 360 feet long and 127 feet wide, while the third of slightly smaller dimensions was to form a T on the shore end of the pier. That was the equivalent of four city blocks of three-story substantial business buildings so constructed that, if immersed in water, they would float.

The project looked good on paper but the question arose, Where could those giant units be built? How could they be transported to their ultimate position at the foot of Fifteenth Street and the Hudson River? Scouts on planes, trains, automobiles and on foot scoured the area within a hundred miles of New York City for a favorable building site.

One day one of the scouts hit upon the ideal location on the banks of the Hudson thirty-five miles north of the metropolis. Grassy Point was singled out. It was there that James A. Farley, former Postmaster General, was born and raised on the main street that was actually a dike between the mile-wide Hudson and an abandoned clay-pit that the rains of years had flooded.

Some 3000 feet long and nearly half as wide, the bottom of this "lake" would give ample elbow-room for the big assignment. But first it must be drained of some 400 million gallons of water. Pumps with a capacity of 12,000 gallons a minute, were set up. In twenty days the lake bottom was dry land far below the level of the adjoining Hudson and so became the largest dry-dock in history.

After 250,000 square feet had been graded and surfaced and a drainage system completed, building was begun. Meanwhile at the other end of the project thirty-eight miles away a corps of divers worked like beavers under water, removing thousands of snaggled piles and laying down a blanket of stone, gravel and sand upon which the gigantic "boxes" could rest snugly on their arrival from the building site up river.

In eighteen months from the time the contract was signed, word went out that moving day was at hand. The big boxes would start on their thirty-eight-mile journey to their new home on the New York City waterfront.

Spectators flocked from miles around to witness the miracle of floating the huge structures of concrete and steel. Few believed it could be done. An elderly farmer remarked, "No use trying to defy the laws of Nature. They might as well try to move the Empire State building up to Yonkers." But the engineers had figured out to a nicety just what would happen. And it did, exactly as they had predicted.

Through a thirty-inch pipe leading from the river to the

natural dry dock, thousands of tons of water cascaded madly. The dried-up lake began to take on its old appearance with water almost from bank to bank. The three concrete structures, rising from its center, seemed to be as firmly anchored as the pyramids. The doubting Thomases murmured, "I told you so!"

Not until the water had reached a depth of nineteen feet did success seem possible. The smallest of the units moved ever so slightly. It was afloat. Soon all three were off the bottom and buoyant as boats at their moorings. A floating dredge, capable of removing a truck-load of dirt at a single bite, was towed into position in order to cut a channel through the embankment separating the lake and the river now on the same level. Waiting tugs took the boxes in tow and the thirty-eight-mile journey to their new position began.

Fourteen hours later the first of the floating monsters arrived at its destination at the exact moment of high tide. It was wedged into place, divers acting as "seeing eyes" under water, engineers with transits directing the surface operation with mathematical precision.

The other units arrived on succeeding tides and were placed with miraculous adjustment where they were secured against lateral movement by steel piles driven deep into the river bottom through "wells" in the structures—a precaution against the tremendous pressures of currents, storm-winds and tide-driven icefields.

And so was finished a stupendous construction project that was without precedent and to which the diver was as essential as the engineer or the builder.

In contrast to the orderly and professionally planned construction type of job, the diver is sometimes an important factor in a salvage operation that calls for courage and stamina in a toe-to-toe battle against natural forces. Just as in the days of the sea-rovers, Captain Kidd and Sir Henry Morgan, ships bearing treasure of great value still sail the Seven Seas. And today, as in days of old, disaster in one form or another sends them to the bottom—to treasure-laden "Davy Jones' Locker."

A typical example of a modern treasure-ship meeting her end and the commercial treasure hunt that followed, is that of a passenger-cargo ship stranded a few years ago off the California coast. In its strong-room was stored some $175,000 in bars of gold and silver bullion and coins.

A radio call for assistance brought the Merritt Chapman & Scott salvage ship *Peacock*, which was six hundred miles distant, hurrying to the scene of the wreck off Santa Marguerita Island.

On the *Peacock's* arrival it was learned that the sunken vessel's six passengers and crew had been taken off safely by another vessel. Led by Salvage Officer Robert Gardner, three officers from the foundered ship returned to the wreck. Only its forward deck and a part of the superstructure were above water and these were being battered by boarding seas. Cargo hold, engine room and all below deck were flooded. The vessel lay on the bottom with a list to port of thirty degrees.

The purser's office was submerged. The heavy surge of the seas made it impossible for a diver to enter in order to retrieve the safe in which were kept the keys to the strong-room. The strong-room itself was also impossible to reach because of the wild surge of water in the passageway leading to it. There was, however, a door to it from the submerged number-four hatch trunk.

Work began at once. The hatch was cleared and diving gear taken aboard. A platform was built and slung into number-four hold. A diver had no difficulty finding the iron door fitted tightly into its metal frame. As a security precaution the door had been barred and locked on the inside. Entry could be made only by forcing the door from its frame. Driving iron wedges between them proved ineffectual after hours of hard labor under water. That plan of attack was abandoned. All hands returned to the salvage ship. Meantime the Merritt Chapman and Scott ship *Homer* had left San Pedro for the scene of the wreck.

For two days, half a gale and high seas made boarding the foundered craft impossible. The *Peacock* left for Magdalena Bay to pick up a quantity of dynamite to be used in breaking into the strong-room.

The *Peacock* returned the following day only to find that the wreck had broken in two. The forward part lay on its side; the after section had a list to starboard of about sixty degrees; both were rolling heavily. The huge seas, now with access to the holds, were sluicing out large amounts of cargo, much of which floated and was recovered by the *Peacock*.

For several days the weather showed no signs of abating and the wreck was settling deeper into the water. An underwriter's agent who had come on the scene, decided it was impractical and dangerous to attempt to salvage the vessel's valuables under such conditions. And so, while waiting for the weather to moderate, the *Homer* left the wreck and headed for San Pedro to be fitted out with underwater cutting gear and other equipment necessary for continuing the salvage operation.

In the interim Captain John Johnson, accompanied by Master Diver H. A. Groves, was dispatched from New York to supervise a new salvage assault on the wreck. Two weeks elapsed before the weather was favorable for the resumption of the work.

When the *Homer* returned to the scene, the wreck had disappeared under the surface of the sea. To fix its exact location soundings were made all around it and buoys were placed to mark its position. Then a diving scow was moored over it.

Before operations began, however, a driving storm whipped in from the Pacific, stampeding high seas before it. The *Homer*, to avoid being stranded, also moored over the wreck. Luckily the blow was short-lived. The salvage work began in earnest.

Two divers, working in concert, found that the storms had left the wreck a shambles. After several attempts, while battling the surging water on the bottom, they located what was left of the battered strong-room, its sides literally torn apart, its valuable contents strewn over the ocean floor. Only a chest of coins and a mail bag were found in the ruins. The rest of the treasure was scattered on the muddy bottom under a tangle of twisted wreckage.

It took several days of blasting with explosives to clear away the mass of metal and debris that surrounded what was once the strong-room. Then came the first inkling of success. The divers, struggling in the violent underwater turbulence, found the first bar of gold. Before the day was over, twenty-five more ingots were recovered.

During the next few days more bars and coins were sifted out of the mud and ooze. But the work was slow and tedious since the treasure was scattered over a large area.

Meeting the resistance of the sunken ship, the moderate sea that was running created a surging turmoil under water that gave the divers anxious moments as they probed among the jagged fragments of the vessel's steel plates. A torn diving dress or badly-fouled lines has brought tragedy under similar conditions.

Some idea of the destructive force of the sea can be gleaned from the fact that many coins, when caught in the tremendous pressure of the bent plates, were found crumpled like tissue paper.

More bad weather was threatening; an "air syphon" was built to expedite the recovery of loose coins and the removal of mud and bottom debris that was suspected of covering much of the treasure. An air syphon is nothing more than a huge vacuum-cleaner that sucks up loose matter. With this modern appliance more than $10,000 in coins were recovered. One hundred and seventy-two bars of bullion were retrieved by the *Homer*'s divers.

To permit continuous operations, the *Peacock* was utilized as a kind of dispatch boat. It brought provisions and explosives to the *Homer* and transported recovered treasure to port. During those trips the bullion and coins were stowed in the lower hold, its steel hatch-cover welded in place to circumvent possible "hi-jackers."

During the following week fifty-six bars of gold and $5,000 in coin were recovered. Later search for the six bars still missing proved fruitless. The threatened storm broke with such unusual violence, the *Homer* ran to cover in Magdalena Bay. It had recovered 230 out of 236 gold bars buried in the sea bottom. It had retrieved $14,837 out of $16,380 in coins from the twisted wreckage of the strong-room.

As the salvage vessel lay at safe anchor well protected from the gale, many a strange story was told of peril and imminent death. A diver, while probing through the tangled debris, was swept off his feet and heaved into a twisted pile of steel plates once a part of a bulkhead. The impact of his body displaced a mass of blasted metal hanging precariously overhead. As it fell he was jerked bodily from where he lay and flung into a towering heap of steel buckled and distorted by the dynamite. He felt the ragged metal claw savagely along his diving dress and waited moment by moment to feel the chill of the water rushing in through a rent in the fabric. Luck was with him; the dress was undamaged.

He pulled hard on his life-line but found it was fouled. His air supply diminished; evidently his air-line had been pinched in the wreckage.

Breathing became more and more difficult. He jerked on his life-line again and again but received no answering pull from his tender. Then a thought struck him—the second diver who could have come to his aid, had left that morning on board the *Peacock* to spend the day ashore. He realized then he was in serious trouble.

But divers have a way of accepting trouble without getting panicky. One by one he tried every escape trick known to his trade. All were unsuccessful. The water around him became vicious. A surge swept over him, putting a strain on his trapped lines.

A succession of heavier surges followed, each a little wilder than its predecessor. A large section of the ship's side, torn from its fastenings, swayed under the intermittent pressures. Some of its motion was transferred to the mass of metal from which it rose. The danger of his lines being cut by the movement of the metal that held them increased. His years of experience told him that the perilous surges were caused by violent squalls that whipped the surface of the sea to a fury.

Just as his hopes were beginning to wane, an unusually violent surge again nearly swept him from his feet and the piled-up metal swayed crazily back and forth under the impact. For a moment he thought his time had come. Then suddenly without warning he felt his lines slacken. The convulsive motion had opened the jaws of the trap that held them. He was free.

He signaled his tender with his life-line to "stand by" and

made his way, slowly and cautiously, out of the danger area. Another signal, "Coming up!" was answered "Okay!" on the life-line.

Minutes later while the diver was being undressed on the diving scow by his faithful and thoroughly frightened tender, the salvage officer came along and asked, "Anything wrong down there?"

The diver smiled and answered, "Nope. Nothing that a little patience couldn't cure whenever you're in a tight spot. How's the coffee?"

It was inevitable that its long years of experience in the salvage field and all the skills employed in it should lead Merritt Chapman & Scott into the broader field of construction ashore and afloat. At first its building operations were confined to projects that involved underwater know-how. So thorough, precise and often daring was its work that its fame spread rapidly and its construction business grew accordingly. Today its contracts on hand mount into hundreds of millions of dollars. Its Black Horse insignia, known all over the world, flies over all its activities and all its ponderous equipment.

Curious about the origin of the symbolic galloping black horse, I learned that it dates back to 1860 when it was used by Captain Israel J. Merritt on his first salvage vessel to honor the "Pony express of the beaches,"—the farmers and fishermen who lived along the coast and who dashed on horseback to the nearest alarm point to summon aid whenever they sighted a ship in distress.

During a visit to the headquarters of the Merritt Chapman & Scott Corporation in midtown Manhattan, I found myself in the midst of modernism in business carried to its ultimate. In offices and areas, laid out as meticulously as a chess-board, scores of people were engaged in their numerous and varied activities without a suggestion of hubbub or haste. Every-

where was the same unhurried deliberateness I had observed
in the salvage operations I had witnessed. There were no
closed doors, no hideaways, no sanctums. Everything was
in the open under stimulating fluorescent lighting softened by
the warm gray tints that enveloped the place. Yet underneath
the calm one felt spirit and drive. Executives and secretaries,
engineers and draughtsmen, specialists in a dozen activities,
even the usual complement of office help exuded alertness and
pride in their many jobs.

Here and there were exquisitely made scale models of many
salvage craft, including their giant derricks "Constitution,"
"Monarch" and "California" with a combined lifting capacity
of 490 tons. On the walls were many dramatic photographs
of operations without precedent in the construction field.
One in particular intrigued me. To my layman's eye it showed
what appeared to be a giant thermos bottle encased in a tight-
fitting square carton. It was being towed by three powerful
tugs.

"What is that?" I asked the official who was showing me
around.

"That," he replied, "is a section of a vehicular tunnel at
the moment of launching. It was towed 180 miles down
Chesapeake Bay to the tunnel site."

Since I had spent some time with the "sand hogs" burrow-
ing under the East River while they were constructing the
midtown tunnel that now connects Manhattan and Brooklyn,
I was completely mystified. It was difficult to visualize a tunnel built 180 miles from the point where it was to lie under
the bottom of a deep and much-traveled river.

"Will you tell me something about it?" I asked.

Here in brief is the startling tale of a tunnel as it was told
to me:

A serious traffic bottleneck existing between Norfolk and

Portsmouth, Virginia, was broken when a tunnel was constructed under the Elizabeth River separating the two communities. Few of the tens of thousands of motorists who later sped through the underwater highway, realized the countless problems and complexities that marked its construction.

The river was deep, nearly a hundred feet; the bottom consisted of alluvial mud deposited through the ages to a great depth. The usual procedure of tunneling under the river bed was proved to be impractical. As an alternative it was decided to build a 3000-foot steel-and-concrete tube extending from shore to shore and to bury this tube in a mammoth trench fifty feet wide and fifty feet deep dredged in the bottom of the river. To accommodate two lanes of traffic as well as ventilating and drainage systems, the tube had an external diameter of thirty-five feet, the approximate height of a three-story building.

To construct the tube in 300-foot sections, as called for by the engineers, it was necessary to employ the services and facilities of the Bethlehem Steel Company's shipyard at Sparrows Point, Maryland. The sections, each as large as an average ocean-going steamship, were built on the usual ways. Upon completion the sections slid down into the water in the same manner as a ship at the moment of launching.

The tube sections were composed of an outer and an inner steel shell with a space of four feet between them. This space was later filled in with thousands of tons of concrete.

Before taking to the water the sections were stoppered at both ends by steel bulkheads that made them water-tight and insured their buoyancy. A thousand tons of concrete ballast was poured into the bottom of each section to keep it right-side-up. To lessen the impact of the water against the forward bulkheads in their initial plunge from the ways, streamlined bows were attached to each section.

Meanwhile the huge trench in which the completed tube was to be laid was dredged with surgical precision. Under the direction and supervision of divers, the bottom of the big ditch was covered with a resilient bed of sand on which the tube could rest comfortably.

As the 300-foot sections slid down the ways and into the water, they were picked up by tugs, and so began their long journey to the tunnel site.

With 600 tons of steel in each of the massive cylinders and 1000 tons of concrete ballast in its belly, the unwieldy tube sections presented a towing problem that called for skill and seamanship. Each of the seven sections required two and sometimes three tugs to escort and guide it to its appointed position while the tugs contended with tides, currents and winds and avoided ever-changing shoals and bars that might prove death traps in the event of grounding.

Arriving at the scene of the tunnel operation, each tube section was tied up at the M. C. & S. "shape up" pier where its interior was lined with an eighteen-inch layer of concrete. A twenty-two-foot concrete roadway was built for its entire length.

Then more concrete was poured into the space between the inner and outer shells until the tube began to sink under the tremendous weight. With only a foot or so out of water, it was towed out and over the exact position it was to occupy in the trench. Then still more concrete was poured in until it sank beneath the surface. Slings from floating derricks supported it as it was lowered gently, under the direction of divers, into the precise spot it was to occupy.

As each of the tube sections was lowered into its final resting place, it was joined to its neighbor by bolts as big around as a man's wrist. This operation was carried on by divers who also guided into place forms for solid rings of concrete around the joints to make the tubes watertight. On the inside of the tunnel the joints were welded together.

When the seventh section was duly lowered and bolted, a continuous tube of steel and concrete extended from shore to shore. The bulkheads that, by excluding the water, enabled the ponderous cylinders to float, were removed with cutting torches and at last men could walk dry-shod under the river from one city to another.

There was much work yet to be done before the tunnel was ready for traffic. It was mostly construction of a conventional nature that was completed with the usual dispatch. Today two lanes of traffic roll through the big tube. Not one in a thousand of those who use it daily realize that it was actually built in a shipyard 180 miles away.

While the professional diver is paid well for his services, his earnings are predicated on many conditions. If he is in the steady employ of a company such as Merritt Chapman and Scott, he receives basic pay like any other employee. His total earnings, however, are based on certain agreements that vary with the conditions under which he works. The number and depths of his dives, the hazards to be encountered, and the character and extent of the work to be done under water all add to the content of his pay envelope.

5   DEEP DOWN UNDER

So far we have dealt with depths that, according to modern diving practice, are comparatively shallow. According to the best scientific authorities, including the British Admiralty and the United States Navy, depths below one hundred and twenty feet are charged with danger for all but the most robust and experienced of divers, particularly if the period of submersion is of long duration and the expenditure of physical effort great.

It is true that divers in conventional rubber diving dress have gone down into far greater depths without serious results, but they are rare exceptions. For instance, a United States Navy submarine, lost with all hands in the Pacific, was discovered lying on the bottom at a depth of 360 feet.

On the salvage ship a Navy diver of long experience volunteered to go down for an exploratory survey. Knowing the desperate chances involved, the Commanding Officer demurred, but later consented on the diver's assurance that he would not venture below a point at which he would sense trouble.

Now it is a known fact that even at extreme depths the diver suffers no serious inconvenience as long as he gets plenty of air and his lines are free. In this instance, however, the unforeseen happened. The diver became trapped in the wreckage of the "sub." Although one of the most expert divers in the service, he was unable to free himself. Equipped with a telephone, he described his predicament to the petty officer in charge of the diving operation. It seemed his chance of release would depend on the assistance of another diver. In reply to the often asked question "How are you feeling?" he repeated the same answer, "Okay, feeling fine."

A comrade, also a man of wide experience under water, volunteered to go down to the rescue of his shipmate. Since the depth was greater than that of any recorded dive in rubber dress, the C.O., fearful of a second mishap, again hesitated to give permission but finally conceded.

Anxious moments on the salvage ship followed the descent of the rescue diver. While still far from the bottom, his telephone failed, his life-rope became his only means of signaling the surface.

As his leaden boots touched the coral-encrusted bottom, he
groped through the darkness to the all but invisible submarine.
More by touch than sight he learned that the craft lay at an
angle of thirty degrees; her bow rested on an overhanging ledge
with a heavy list to starboard. In her bilge was a ragged hole
as large as a doorway and almost level with the ocean floor.
Through this opening the lines of the trapped diver led into
the interior and a jumbled mass of metal, evidently the result
of an explosion. Cautious as a stalking cat, the rescue diver
crawled through a confusion of wrecked machinery and soon
came upon his shipmate pinned under a heavy control-panel
torn from its fastenings.

Running his hands over the imprisoned man's arms, legs
and torso, as if feeling for broken bones, he discovered no
injury. The mass of metal holding the first diver down lay
squarely across his breastplate. From the valve in his helmet
the exhaust air was rising in a column of bubbles.

With the calmness born of years of experience in such emergencies, the rescuer tested the weight of the imprisoning
metal at several points and then with caution attempted to
lift it, gently at first and then with all the strength of his powerful frame. Somewhere in the deep gloom something gave
way. The metal panel and the gear attached to it became
lighter as he continued to lift. Presently he could feel the
twistings and turnings of the captive diver as he extricated
himself from the trap that held him. A strong pat on the
shoulder told the rescuer his man was free.

As the divers escaped from the stricken sub and groped their
way to the diving stage—the metal platform on which they had
been lowered and which would now take them to the surface
—they realized that the most perilous part of the operation lay
ahead of them. Only a miracle of sound judgment on the

In the following 15 pages authentic photographs show divers and diving operations. They were supplied by the U.S. Navy, Standard Oil New Jersey, Merritt Chapman & Scott Corporation, Fenjohn Underwater Photo and Equipment Company. Drawings of diving shells are by the author.

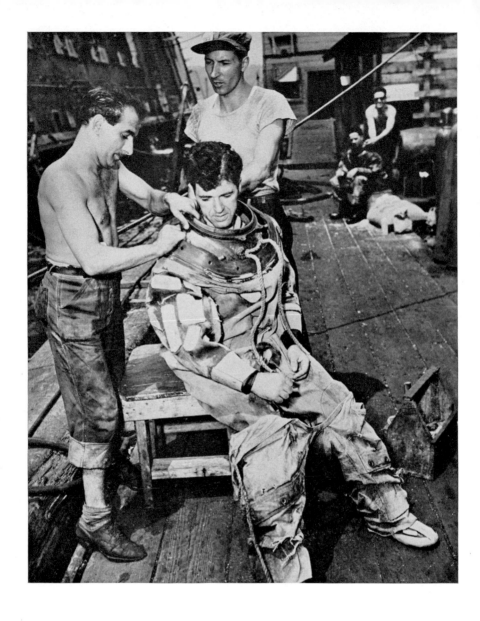

A faithful tender "dresses" a Navy diver with meticulous care in preparation for a dive to the sunken *Normandie*.

The diver's work does not always take him into the clean and limpid water of the sea. Here is a diver descending into a murky river fouled by the sewage of a great city.

Thirty to forty pounds of lead and leather go
into the making of the diver's shoes. This weight
on his feet is necessary to keep him right side up.
Note the heavy metal toe guards that protect his
feet from injury.

A modern version of the diving bell is about to be lowered from the U.S.S. *Tringa* for the rescue of men in a helpless submarine. Open at the bottom, it is secured over an escape hatch on the sub. It will accommodate several of the rescued men.

Diver descending to make final inspection of emergency repair on vessel with a large hole stove in
her side. Without the skills and uncanny know-
how of the diver, such jobs would be all but
impossible.

Men at work. This giant derrick barge has come to grips with a sunken tug. Having placed wire slings under the tug's hull, the diver comes up to confer with company officials. At a signal, hoisting begins and a dead weight of 140 tons, the equivalent of 75 modern automobiles, is lifted to the surface.

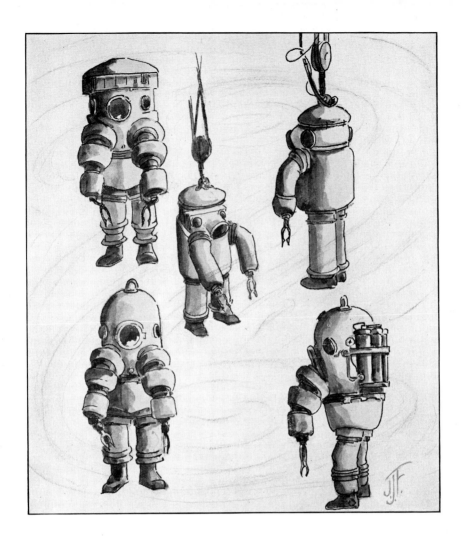

Diving shells from earliest to latest model
(*center*). Looking like monsters from another
planet, these suits of heavy steel armor are worn
by divers at great depths that would prove fatal
in conventional rubberized diving dress.

Divers on the submarine rescue vessel *Greenlet,* ready to be lowered on diving stage into deep water off Pearl Harbor. It is a part of the constant training that keeps these men alert and fit for any rescue or salvage call that may come.

The sunken *Normandie* during the process of raising it. One of the greatest salvage operations of our time, it presented numerous problems for which there was no precedent. Many of the world's best divers received their initial training in the diving school set up at the scene of the wreck.

Free as a fish in its native element, the aqualung swimmer prowls in search for photogenic subjects. His underwater motion picture camera is housed in metal and glass to withstand the crushing pressure to which it may be subjected. Sheath knife at his belt is carried not only as a tool but as a defensive weapon.

Photo shows a typical diving scene. The huge
pipes are lowered by the derrick barge to the river
bottom and in perfect alignment. Such operations
would not be possible without the assistance of
divers, two of whom, up for a breather, are in
conference on the float alongside the barge.

Here is one of the seven 300-foot sections of the vehicular tunnel connecting Norfolk and Portsmouth, Virginia. Built 180 miles from the tunnel site, they were towed to their final position and sunk through 90 feet of water into a huge trench across the bottom of a busy river.

Underwater demolition team paddles toward the beach at Wonsan, Korea. Under the placid surface of the water lie hundreds of deadly mines that must be exploded before troops may attempt to land.

After inspection of the water for mines and other obstacles, this demolition unit hauls its rubber boat up on the beach to continue the search for death traps, preparatory to landing troops.

An underwater demolition squad at Iwon, Korea,
searches the water for hidden obstacles and measures its depth before ships in background send
invasion troops to the beach.

salvage ship, while they were being hoisted, could save them from an attack of the "bends" that might cripple or kill them.

Thanks to our Navy's strict observance of the decompression formula for ascent, neither of the men suffered any ill effects from their adventure. As a precaution, however, they were given a period in the decompression chamber.

In the earlier days of diving when men depended upon a hand-operated air-pump, many a diver in deep water fell unconscious because of an insufficient air supply. With the power-driven air compressor came greater safety at greater depths. At a depth of one hundred and twenty feet, for instance, the diver is subjected to a pressure of $53\frac{1}{2}$ pounds per square inch and as the depth increases, so does the pressure increase until it reaches a point far beyond the capacity of any hand-operated mechanism.

While chatting recently with Jeremiah Mason, a veteran diver of many years experience in many parts of the world, I asked him what he considered a safe depth at which a diver could work without risking the "bends."

"I wish I knew," he replied. "I've been in this business nearly thirty years and I've seen many cases where men were knocked out by compression, no two of them exactly alike. I've known men who had done heavy work at a depth of a hundred or more feet come through without so much as a twinge, yet I've seen some of them come up from a job at fifty feet in a near state of collapse. Compression does strange things to men who can't take it. Some suffer from double vision or temporary blindness or a disturbance of the nervous system. In most cases, however, it's a simple case of the bends. The only effective remedy is decompression skillfully applied.

"Now don't get me wrong," he continued, "these compression diseases are becoming comparatively rare. This is due to improved equipment, better training and more scientific supervision. Take my own case, for instance. I have never been laid up an hour as a result of my work under water, and that goes too for most of the divers I know. Of course there are some people who are prone to accident whether they be in the water or out of it. To those I would say 'Let the other fellow do the diving!' "

Even at its best the usefulness of the conventional rubberized dress is limited by the depth of the water in which it is to be used. There are experts who insist that its use at a depth of more than one hundred and twenty feet, except in rare instances, is scarcely worth the effort. Below that depth few divers are capable of heavy work. Their movements and even their mental processes are slowed down and the extreme length of their air- and life-lines subject them to the whims and whirls of currents and the normal motion of the water.

Notwithstanding its limitations, the conventional diving dress has numerous advantages. It gives the diver ample mobility. He can walk, stoop, kneel, crawl, lie on his back or on his belly or assume any position demanded by the work he is doing. By regulating his air outlet valve, he can inflate his dress to any desired degree, thus giving himself controlled buoyancy. In this way he can make prodigious leaps in slow motion. If, for instance, he is inspecting a wreck on the bottom and he wishes to reach the deck forty feet above him, he closes the outlet valve on his helmet and permits the incoming air to inflate his dress. In a moment or two he has the sensation of having no weight. Then giving himself a gentle thrust upward with his legs, he soars gracefully to the desired height and lowers himself to the deck simply by allowing his air flow to take its normal course. With his hands and arms free he can use the many tools of the various trades in which he is skilled or perform the many other duties to which he may be assigned.

And so the "close" diving dress invented by Siebe nearly a hundred years ago is used throughout the world for many different purposes, from sponge-fishing to bridge-building. It is only man's inability to withstand extreme pressures that has set a sharp limit on its use.

In many parts of the world the ocean floor is littered with what were once proud ships, many of them with riches in their holds and strong-rooms. Lost in war or storm or collision or from causes unknown, this ghost armada has beckoned treasure hunters for more than a century. Now and then a sunken ship proved a rich prize for salvagers when it lay in shallow water but it served also as a lure to tempt men to pry into greater depths where an estimated million-dollar hoard was theirs for the taking.

Many a futile attempt was made to harvest a portion of the wealth, and many a daring diver left his bones to rot among those of the men who went down with their ship.

It was common knowledge that the pressure at great depths was the barrier that baffled men in their attempts to conquer the lower regions of the ocean. How to protect the diver from this pressure became a much-debated question among the treasure hunters.

The flexible diving dress had proved itself a death-trap at depths below a certain level. Men who had ventured down into the danger zone and were raised quickly to the surface suffered or died of a mysterious malady. Decompression, if applied at all, was rudimentary.

Inventors in various countries turned their talents to the development of a rigid suit of metal that would defy the crushing pressure encountered in deep water. In 1875 a Frenchman exhibited a "diving dress" that resembled a suit of medieval armor. It was made of sheet iron beautifully burnished and ornamented. To demonstrate it, he had arranged to have himself lowered into a deep hole in the Seine a short distance outside Paris. He had been under water scarcely more than a minute when he signaled madly on his life-line to be hauled up. As he was lifted from the river, water poured from the iron suit as from a leaky bucket. Another minute or two under water and he would have been drowned in his own brain child.

Spurred by the prospect of garnering vast wealth from the ocean depths, a dozen other inventors from several other countries worked frantically on designs that would defy pressure. All agreed on metal as the medium. The result of their labors was a collection of hideous and impractical creations that leaked at the joints, that were so cumbersome the wearers were unable to perform even the simplest tasks. All the rigid suits conformed to the shape of the human body. Head, torso, arms and legs were protected individually.

In one of the tests the diver was lowered into the Mediterranean. By a strange mischance he landed in the hold of an ancient vessel. A man of long experience under water, he probed through the murky gloom and discovered what seemed to be a number of small casks all heavily encrusted with sea growth. In his effort to dislodge one of them, a seam weakened in the metal of his armor. With the possibility of an escaping air supply, he signaled to be hauled to the surface. His life-line grew taut. His feet left the ooze on the floor of the hull. He felt himself rising slowly through the black shadows. His helmet struck some object above him and glanced off only to be caught between two overhanging deck planks. The upward pull on his life-line increased until he could feel it press the thin metal of his armor against his sides. His tenders, sensing the resistance on the line, ceased hoisting and soon received a signal from below, "More air!"

Encased in the rigid outfit that did not permit him to raise his arms above his shoulders, the diver could not attempt to free himself nor could he determine what held him prisoner. ' He could, however, give his body a slight swinging motion since it was free below his shoulders. Luckily his tender from long experience understood his predicament. He tried pulling on the line at various angles, as one would try to free a fishing-hook snagged on the bottom of a stream.

Although the long immersion was beginning to tell on the trapped man, the divers' philosophy, "While there's life, there's hope," was strong within him, even though at the moment he was helplessly encased like a sardine in a tin.

As the pulling and hauling on his life-line continued, he feared that the injured seam might open up under the strain. That would have meant the end, for the capacity of the hand-operated air-pump would not have been sufficient to compensate for the outrush of air through the ruptured seam.

After an age-long hour of entrapment he felt his life-line pull him in a backward direction. His hopes rose high as he became conscious of his metal helmet scraping over the salt-encrusted deck-planks that held him fast. A few more lusty pulls and he was free. After a leisurely ascent to the surface, he was taken safely on board his ship. Even before his metal suit could be removed, he told of the casks he had discovered and of their exact position.

At first, in salvage circles, his exploit was considered merely as a brave attempt but a complete failure. As wiser heads thought about it, however, it opened up new vistas and sent the designers of diving gear off on a new line of attack.

Soon after this there appeared an obscure inventor who declared that the *arch* was Nature's own design for pressure resistance. To demonstrate his theory, he placed an egg between his palms and with all his strength applied pressure to its long axis. The fragile egg remained intact. Its perfect arch enabled it to resist the pressure.

Almost immediately there was a revolution in the designs of diving gear for the great depths where rich treasure lay. The firm of Siebe, Gorman & Company of London, successors to Siebe the inventor of the "close" diving dress, designed an apparatus on the arch principle. It consisted of a metal cylinder crowned and based with domes resembling the ends of an egg. It was provided with observation windows, a searchlight, an air purifier, oxygen tanks and telephone. It accommodated a single diver who acted not as a laborer but as an observer who could direct the mechanical operations of a salvage ship, fully equipped with many kinds of demolition and recovery mechanisms capable of ripping apart decks and superstructures, tearing down bulkheads and dredging deep in the holds where the cargo lay. All this was under the direction of the observer deep down under in the security of his metal "shell." The term "shell" is said to have originated in the egg experiment.

While the Siebe, Gorman shell proved moderately successful in many salvage operations, it also had many limitations. Its occupant was powerless to perform even the simplest physical tasks. Aware of this, the German firm of Neufeldt and Kuhnke set about designing a shell that would enable a diver to perform certain light but most important labor—the accurate placing of explosives to blast the hull of a wreck, the gathering of coins, bars of gold, jewels or other valuables scattered on the bottom or the performance of other task that did not require unusual strength or endurance.

The German model of the diving shell might truly be called the most hideous contraption ever devised by man. From its huge cylindrical body topped by a dome with staring window eyes, protruded two metal arms and legs resembling the shapeless fore- and hind legs of a mastodon. It carried on its back, knapsack fashion, a cluster of oxygen bottles to enrich the air supply. The diver's hands were encased in metal sleeves jointed only at the shoulders. To enable the occupant to perform manual tasks, a kind of forceps projected through watertight couplings from the end of each sleeve. These pincers were operated from inside the sleeves by the diver's hands. In short, this diving shell was a machine that derived its working power from the man sealed within it. In its developed form the Neufeldt and Kuhnke articulated shell proved successful in actual use.

In a search for a sunken submarine a young diver hung up a new record for depth and time under water. The feat spurred the deep-water salvagers to new effort. Here at last was their answer to an age-old problem. French and Italian contractors were quick to secure rights to the use of the latest design of diving shell. The Italians were first to reap a rich harvest from a cargo vessel sunk in the Mediterranean some two miles off Genoa in 350 feet of water. It was an operation of considerable magnitude since it took nearly four years to complete. Despite bad weather that often interrupted the work, more than 7000 tons of valuable cargo were removed and sold at market prices. The holds of the vessel were literally packed solid with steel bars, assorted machinery, copper ingots and railroad equipment including a number of locomotives. Only the ungainly diving shell made possible the recovery of such a vast amount of costly material.

It was by mere chance that I had met a diver who had worked for more than a year on that salvage job. We were both passengers on a steamship bound for Colombia. Like other divers I had met, he was inclined to be uncommunicative except when he was discussing the prestige of his profession and the incompetence of engineers who had never donned a diving dress but who professed to know more about underwater work than men who had spent a lifetime in it.

One evening while we were in the Caribbean headed for the port of Cartagena, we were seated on deck. For no apparent reason his tongue loosened. In a confiding voice scarcely above a whisper he told me that the calm moonlit sea, the balmy air and the gentle swishing of the ship's bow-wave reminded him of his youth and of his father Guiseppi Bossi, a diver of fame in every Mediterranean port. It was from him he had learned the skills and risks of the diver's trade. There was a note of grief in his voice as he told me of his father's death, the result of a premature explosion during a salvage operation on a sunken vessel off the coast of Corsica.

I ventured a question. "Why did you take up such a dangerous profession?"

There was a note of disdain in his answer. "Danger is ever present in life," he said. "The prick of a rusty needle, a fall downstairs, a speeding automobile may bring crippling or death. The steamship *Titanic* sank with fifteen hundred souls aboard just because a mass of polar ice strayed into her path and ripped her wide open. Each day's newspapers carry stories of people hurt and killed, but you'll notice in almost every case, someone was negligent or careless. During my thirty years in the business of diving I never knew a sober steady man to lose a day's work as a result of accident. That was because he kept his wits about him."

After a short silence I felt the urge to start him on his life story. "When did you begin your diving career?" I inquired.

"Actually in 1921," he replied. "I was then a husky lad of

nineteen. But previous to that I had often acted as assistant tender for my father. I could handle his lines and help in dressing him. Once while slipping on his helmet, I allowed it to scrape his nose and I'll never forget the blistering lecture he gave me afterward. Even when I was a kid in short pants, I was as familiar with diving gear as the boys of today with football togs. When not in use, my father's diving dress and his heavy woolen underwear hung on the family clothes-line for 'airing.' Although the dress is waterproof, condensation and perspiration create much dampness on the inside.

"On the morning of my nineteenth birthday a contractor for whom my father had done a number of diving jobs, came to our door. 'Come along, Bossi!' he said. 'A small barge has sunk in the harbor. She's loaded with government supplies. Ammunition, I believe. She's lying near number four buoy in thirty feet. We've got to get slings under her. A derrick barge is already on its way to the spot.'

"My father, a man of few words, turned to me and said, 'Get out the spare gear. I'll need help.'

"It was as if he had said to me, 'Here are a thousand lire. Go out and enjoy yourself.' Light-hearted, I helped load the contractor's truck. On our way to the waterfront we stopped to pick up Giovanni, my father's faithful tender. When he learned I was about to make my first dive, he growled through his beard 'It's about time,' and then resumed his usual silence. A roomy working boat took us out to the scene of the sinking. A huge derrick barge was standing by.

"With the aid of two tenders my father and I were soon in diving dress. Before the helmets were secured to our breastplates my father said, 'Take it easy for a while, till you get used to the air.' Then with helmet and weighted belt firmly adjusted, he lumbered to the ladder lowered from the boat gunwale and disappeared under the surface. As my helmet was lowered over my head and secured, I was enveloped in a strange silence broken only by the gentle hiss of air escaping through the regulating valve. I soon noticed that the air smelled of rubber and machine oil with a whiff of garlic of which my father, who had last worn the helmet, was excessively fond. After an interminable ten minutes, my tender tapped my helmet twice. It meant 'Let's go!' and was in obedience to a prearranged signal from my father. An eighty pound leaden belt was secured around my waist, life-line and air-line were double checked. As I moved toward the descending ladder, I felt like Atlas with the world on his shoulders. My total weight at that moment was close to four hundred pounds.

"As I descended the ladder, rung by rung, I had the strange sensation of losing weight with every step till I felt as light as a small boy. The instant my leaden boots touched the bottom, I sensed a firm grip and a friendly pat on my arm. My father's helmet moved toward mine until they touched, then I heard a far-off voice bellow, 'Keep close and keep your eyes open! You may learn something.'

"While there is rarely more than a foot or two of tide in the Mediterranean, there are strange eddies and currents that the diver must lean against, like a person walking in slow motion against a brisk March wind.

"Through the greenish light coming down from the surface, I watched my father at work, every movement slow, careful and without waste of effort. He handled the heavy wire slings as deftly as if he were wrapping string around a package. He adjusted shackles and hooks with the skill that comes only from experience. When he sent up the signal, 'Hoist away!' the sunken wreck, now suspended from the derrick, rose slowly from the bottom until it was only a black shadow against the sunlit surface.

"The job was finished. Although I had contributed nothing beyond being an observer, I knew in my heart that diving would be my future career. After two years of apprenticeship under my father, I went on my own and with his blessing.

"In the years that followed I made something of a reputation as a good deep-water man. My services were in demand whenever difficult salvage jobs were to be done. And so my work took me to far and strange places. I soon learned that while countries and people differ widely, the world under water differs little except in depth and temperature, whether it be off the shores of Alaska or the coast of Australia eleven thousand miles distant.

"It was near Sydney, Australia, I first saw a diving shell in operation. A vessel had been sunk in a collision some ten miles off the coast. In her safe were negotiable securities, gold coins and jewels to the amount of a quarter million dollars. In her holds was a shipment of top-secret devices that might have proved troublesome in the hands of an unfriendly nation. An underwater survey showed that her bow rested on the top of a precipice at a depth of about a hundred feet, while her stern rested on the bottom a hundred and fifty feet lower, leaving the keel at an angle of about thirty degrees.

"Thanks to thorough instruction from my father in the early days, I had become expert in opening submerged safes without endangering their contents with explosives. It was because of my success in this work that I was employed by the salvage company.

"The safe was in the captain's cabin. I found it to be a huge affair of ancient pattern and as simple to open as a suitcase. I set to work immediately under the glare of a battery floodlight I had taken down with me. Intent on the combination as I turned the dial slowly, I felt something touch my helmet. That was not unusual in confined places undersea where semi-buoyant debris is in constant motion. Presently a pale and wizened human hand appeared outside the front window of my helmet, its fingers clutched as if in agony. I turned my head to look through the window on the side. A bloated face with open mouth and eyes stared at me.

"A slight swirl in the water wafted the apparition into deep shadow. As it passed by almost in the posture of a swimmer, I saw the gold braid of the ship's captain glint in the watery light.

"Now I'm not superstitious nor do I suffer from nerves, but I must confess I lost no time in getting that safe open. When at last the door swung wide and I had checked the contents, I phoned the salvage ship, 'Everything okay in safe. Have found captain's body.' The reply came back, 'Send up body. Let contents of safe wait. Will lower hoisting gear.'

"Soon a wire basket on the end of a stout line landed on the starboard wing of the bridge. Obedient to orders, I prepared to send up the mortal remains of a brave man who feared death less than the loss of his ship. I searched every inch of the cabin for the body but could not find even a trace of it. I was about to report its disappearance when I noticed what might have been a tiny shred of cotton waste caught in the glare of the floodlight. It was moving ever so slowly, borne by a gentle current deflected upward by the cabin bulkhead. I watched it as it rose to the ceiling. Then I saw the shadowy form of what was once the captain still in the posture of a swimmer. It was higher than my clumsy diving dress permitted me to reach, but a turn on the air-escape valve on my helmet inflated my rubber suit enough to give buoyancy and lift me higher to capture the fugitive.

"The body was without the slightest weight as I maneuvered it through cabin and chartroom and bridge to the starboard wing where I cast off the line from the basket and with it clapped a bowline under the armpits. 'Hoist away!' I phoned the salvage ship, adding, 'Stand by to receive a gallant captain coming on board!' "

A passing ship north-bound interrupted the diver's story. Passengers waving hands and handkerchiefs lined the rail, a custom as old as seafaring itself.

When the flurry of excitement had ended, my friend the diver continued. "With my safe-cracking job finished, I found myself with time on my hands. The cargo, which was beyond my depth in flexible diving dress, was in process of removal by deepwater men protected from the heavy pressure in rigid diving shells. Although I had been diving for nearly ten years, I had never been on a job that required shells. Here was my chance to see one in operation and to learn something of its advantages.

"Bright and early one morning, I was on deck. Work on the salvage ship began shortly after daybreak. On the foredeck, suspended on an iron framework, the diving shell swayed slightly with the gentle roll of the vessel. A metal object as large as a manhole cover lay on the deck. In shape it resembled the lid of a giant teakettle. Nearby the diver, a powerful hulk of a man, was struggling into a rubber combination of heavy pants and boots. The many layers of woolen clothing made his body seem bloated. He wore a knitted skullcap at a rakish angle. Two of the crew were busy preparing the shell. They screwed the elephantine arms and legs in place, testing and oiling the joints with the care astronomers take in adjusting a ponderous telescope. Air connections were tightened and tested. Tested also were the diver's telephone and headpiece. A steel bottle of oxygen and one of compressed air were secured in their respective clamps inside the shell. And as a finishing touch a respirator to purify the used air was put in its appointed place.

"The ritual completed, the 'Ready!' signal was given the diver. With a motion strangely resembling a giant gorilla he swung himself up on the iron frame and lowered himself into the shell.

"With ear-phones adjusted and transmitter in hand, the diver gave his indispensable telephone a last-minute test. Then with a wave of the hand he slipped down into the cylinder, putting arms and legs simultaneously into their metal water-tight casings. The kettle-lid or dome that lay on the deck was lifted to the top of the cylinder and secured in place by numerous screw bolts. The pincers protruding from the ends of the metal arms snapped open and shut like the claws of an angry crab.

"Then from the phone came the order 'Lower away!' A block-and-tackle was lowered from the boom on the foremast. A hook engaged the shackle on the top of the dome. The ship's hoisting engine rumbled and the metal monster, looking neither like man nor beast, was swung outboard and lowered gently into the sea. It floated with less than a quarter of its bulk out of water. It looked completely inanimate, until I saw a white cloth wielded by the diver who was wiping off the film of condensation caused by contact with the cold water, on the inside of the shell's inch-thick windows.

"Clear as a bell came the telephoned word from the diver, 'Ready to dive.' The block-and-tackle was cast off and the shell now slung on a slender wire cable that differed from ordinary twisted cables in that its strands were plaited like a little girl's pigtails. The reason? When a great length of twisted cable is paid out, it has a tendency to untwist, thus giving the shell a spinning motion. The braided cable does not do this.

"After a few moments' pause an asthmatic hiss came from the shell as the diver released the air in his ballast tank. The water closed over the dome of the shell that soon became a ghostly shadow, growing fainter as it went deeper.

"As I stood on deck close to the tender, I could hear with earphones every word coming from the diver. He said he was on the afterdeck of the wreck. The starboard plating was badly stove in by the collision. Deck plates, deck beams and hatch covers were a hopeless tangle.

" 'Lower away the hook!' he commanded.

"From the derrick boom on the foremast a ponderous hook thick as a man's arm and painted white was sent down speedily.

"Presently he barked, 'Ease off lowering!' Then 'Lay aft with hook ten feet! So.' And, 'Lower away, easy does it! Hold it!' His voice had the crackle of lightning in it.

"No sound came from the phone for several minutes. The tender whispered, 'He's hooking on to something heavy. I can tell by his voice.'

"The phone squawked, 'Swing me clear of the wreck!'

"The braided cable that led to the diving shell cut a wide curve through the water as it swung the diver out of the danger zone.

"At a signal from the tender, 'Hoist away!' the steam windlass went into clattering action. The wire cables hooked to the wreck grew taut and quivered. As the strain increased, the salvage ship heeled over until its rail was almost awash. It seemed for moments that an irresistible force had met its match in an irresistible object. From bridge to boiler-room, men held their breath as the three-thousand-ton ship bulldogged the burden that lay nearly four hundred feet underneath it.

"After an interminable ten minutes something giving way on the wreck sent a shudder up the cable. It could be felt all over the vessel as she staggered to an even keel. The man at the windlass smiled and began hoisting cautiously.

"The diver phoned, 'Going aboard wreck for a look-see. Give me a lift!' Minutes later he reported, 'You've ripped out deck beam and large section of deck plates. Deposit wreckage on bottom and lower hook!'

"Orders were carried out promptly. The mass of debris was dumped on the ocean floor at a safe distance and the work progressed until mid-morning when a substitute diver replaced the man in the shell. About two bells, one o'clock, all diving was suspended for the day.

"Later I strolled aft to where the number one diver was seated on a coiled hawser. He was busily engaged in knitting a skull-cap similar to those worn by divers everywhere. His fingers were nimble as those of a woman expert.

"When we had chatted awhile I learned he had known my father and had worked with him on a ticklish salvage job many years before. At first he was secretive about the finer points of the work in a diving shell, but gradually he thawed out and answered my questions with frankness.

" 'Tell me,' " I asked, " 'why do you start work so early in the morning and quit so early in the afternoon?'

"He laid aside his knitting as he answered, 'In deep-water work you've got to be careful, not only of what you eat but of when you eat it. We always work on an empty stomach without so much as a cup of coffee.'

"I was reminded of the pearl divers of the Pacific who for generations have pursued their hazardous work on empty stomachs. Always a coffee lover, I asked, 'How does coffee affect a man working in a diving shell?' "

" 'Well,' he said, 'I've known men who mugged up on coffee before going down, get so violently ill, they had to quit. Some put the blame on a faulty respirator, others insisted coffee was the cause of their trouble.'

"We chatted for nearly two hours. I asked many technical questions that would interest only a diver. I received forthright answers in spite of the fact that several of them might be trade secrets. Then the diver yawned as he gathered up his knitting gear. 'I'm going below to hit the sack,' he said apologetically, 'In this business you need plenty of sleep.'

"I remained on deck. I had some serious thinking to do. During our conversation I began to feel that, despite my experience and skill, I was still a second-string diver. Only a few times in my career did my work take me deeper than a hundred feet. I envied the men who were trained and equipped to work at several times that depth. But I also admired them as the pilot of a plane with a ceiling of a few thousand feet admires the men who hurl their jet-propelled craft up to altitudes of fifty thousand or more feet.

"For two exciting days I watched the salvage ship, directed by the diver, tear the steel hulk apart and dip down deep into its holds with clawlike 'grabs' to seize case after case of precious cargo and deposit it on the deck of a barge.

"It was on my last night aboard the salvage vessel I lay awake in my bunk trying to decide on my future course. I debated with myself whether to abandon the traditional diving dress and the heavy labor it entailed or to adopt the more modern and less exacting shell in which the diver acts chiefly as an underwater observer, adviser and often director.

"A pink dawn was peeping through the porthole over my

bunk before I came to a final conclusion. I would cast my future lot with the men who worked in shells.

"Within a week I was on my way to Italy, hopeful of joining a widely known salvage company that specialized in deep sea projects and the extensive use of shells. Again my father's name came to my aid. He had worked for this company many years before and was held in high esteem.

"When I stated my aim frankly, I was told in no uncertain terms it would take some time before I could be entrusted with work in a shell. Meantime I could busy myself with odd jobs including the shallow water diving of my profession.

"During the months that followed I absorbed every crumb of information on the techniques of the shell diver and the mechanics of the shell itself. The fraternal spirit that exists among divers was constantly in evidence. My endless questions were answered cheerfully. They had accepted me as an old hand in the business of diving and credited me with being as skilled in my field as they were in theirs.

"One day when our ship had reached the scene of a wreck and was preparing to begin salvage operations, the boss diver said to me, 'Stand by to go down for a look-see. Check the name of the vessel, her condition, how she lies and the kind of bottom immediately surrounding her.'

"The shell I was to occupy was suspended from its metal bracket in the forward hold. A tender was getting it ready for action while I donned the usual layer-on-layer of woolen and water-proof clothing. At a word from the boss diver I put on the headphones and swung myself up and over the shell opening, then gingerly lowered myself into position. After various routine tests the dome was bolted in place. 'All ready!' I shouted. 'Hoist away!' My voice boomed in the dead silence. It had a strange metallic quality. I could feel the vibrations of the windlass as I was raised from the hold and lowered into the water. My shell floated for a few moments while the hoisting gear was cast off. A turn of a valve released the air ballast with a burbling hiss. Now suspended on the thin braided line, I began to sink.

"Peering through the windows, I discovered that, at a depth of seventy-five feet, the light was excellent, then began to diminish rapidly like the shadow thrown by a dense cloud passing across the sun. Soon, however, the light brightened again. I learned later that the temporary twilight was caused by a vast stratum of microscopic sea-life. A few fathoms farther down a gradual diminishing of the light began and continued until I had reached the bottom. At four hundred feet the darkness resembled a cloud-blanketed midnight on an open stretch of land. Objects were visible only in hazy silhouette at a distance of ten to fifteen feet. When I had reported hitting bottom, a water-tight floodlight of half-a-million candle-power was lowered.

"At first I thought it would be a valuable aid in my survey, but soon I found in spite of its power it was little more effective than a single candle in a dark cathedral nave. However, in its very small way it helped me appraise the condition of the wreck, not by its illumination but by the shadows it cast. The tremendous pressures intensified by the uneasy movement of a wind-harried sea had bent and twisted and fractured hull and superstructure till the vessel resembled an old tin can that had been kicked around by a band of exuberant boys.

"Somewhere in the wreckage a fortune in gold and other valuables was supposed to be hidden, yet many a worthless wreck has been mistaken for a treasure ship. And so my most important duty was to identify beyond all doubt the vessel I was surveying.

"All hands had been briefed in the structural characteristics, deck equipment and fittings of the ship. Those, however, would not provide infallible identification since many wartime ships had been built identical in every detail. Only the ship's name *Varuna* would identify her from all others. That name would be found on the stern in bronze letters two feet tall.

"With no more effort on my part than a telephone order to my tender, I was transported the length of the ship, lowered to within a few feet of the taffrail and soon maneuvered into a position where I could try to make out the name. Meantime seepage of water into the casing had drowned out the light. Like a blind man reading Braille, I ran the pincers on the arm of the shell over the outline of the large metal letters riveted to the ship's stern plates. I was able to decipher the letters V-A-R-U-N. The final A was on a buckled plate out of my reach. But there was no doubt as to the ship's identity.

"And now with my assignment finished, I began my tedious ascent to the surface. During the slow rise I reviewed my first venture into the deep unknown. My first surprise was when I discovered that, in spite of the 800-pound weight and clumsiness of the shell out of water, it allowed me considerable mobility. This was not strange since its weight combined with my own, when under water, was about forty pounds.

"True, I had to walk with a stiff-legged waddle. But the rigid metal sleeves that encased my hands and arms interfered but slightly with my work. Thanks to the purifying respirator and the oxygen with a dash of helium, the air in the shell was good and the 'bends' were less than a remote possibility.

"Within a year after my first shell-dive I was working with the best divers in the business. Since then I've had jobs all over the world wherever difficult salvage operations were carried on . . . You see, I am a business man—diving is my business. And so, like all business men, I keep in touch with those engaged in the same line.

"Perhaps when we go ashore at Cartagena tomorrow, you

would like to come with me to Barranquilla for a visit with my old friend Ricco, one of the greatest divers that ever lived. He retired two years ago and settled down in Colombia, happy as a clam at high tide. I think you'll enjoy meeting him, for he can spin a yarn with the best of them."

"Agreed!" I said eagerly.

6   OLD DIVER'S TALE

Barranquilla is a neat and picturesque city with a population of 150,000. Situated near the mouth of the swift-flowing Magdalena River, it has become in recent years an important Caribbean port. It boasts of many fine houses, hotels and public buildings.

When we arrived on the waterfront, my friend, the diver, led me to the boat landing stage, where we boarded a launch to reach Ricco's home several miles upstream. The river, then in flood, was nearly two miles wide and rushing to the sea at express speed. Uprooted trees and varied flotsam swept by us sometimes too close for comfort. There were moments when our little craft could barely stem the current.

The Magdalena is a river always in a hurry to empty itself of the torrential rains that flow into it for its length of 1000 miles. Reaching the opposite shore and slacker water, we found the river bordered by vast areas of semi-inundated marsh-lands and slimy swamps. There was no sign of human habitation save for a long string of steel barges moored to the riverbank far upstream.

My friend rose from his seat, pointing toward the barges. "There's Ricco's hideaway!" he shouted. "I hope his mooring lines hold in this rampaging river!" Then he explained, "The steel barges were built by an American steamship company for the river trade along its five hundred miles of shallow but navigable water."

There were six 200-foot barges, designed not only for cargo but for passengers too. The barges, costing more than a million dollars, had been laid up at their swampy moorings as a result of a commercial slump. Such valuable property required expert maintenance and supervision during the long-drawn-out period of business doldrums. The ravages of tropical climate, the tantrums of the unpredictable river and the unsettled political atmosphere demanded that a man of strong character and wide experience be put in charge. Ricco was the man.

As we came alongside the number one barge, his foghorn voice bellowed a hearty greeting, his wide-spread arms and winning smile assured us of hospitable welcome.

As he ushered us into his quarters, I was struck by the lavish furnishings. His living-room had been the passengers' salon.

The four adjoining staterooms were used as sleeping quarters by his family—his wife, two grandchildren and their mother—to all of whom we were introduced. There was also a native woman who acted as nursemaid and cook.

It was a comfortable home in a weird setting with the rushing river on one side and the snake-infested swamps on the other and with no other habitation in sight.

After a delicious midday meal my friend the diver and I sat and chatted with Ricco in the shade of an awning on deck. Despite his isolation he was well informed in world affairs through the medium of radio, and somehow he kept up to the minute on the latest developments in the world of salvage. He held forth on the problem of keeping his million-dollar fleet of barges safely moored. The sweeping current harried them day and night while the soft ooze of the marshland made poor holding ground for his land anchors in spite of the miles of steel hawsers he had run out to hold them.

Like many oldtimers who love to compare the accomplishments of men of his day with those of the more modern school, he referred again and again to the heroic struggle of the *Artiglio* and her diving crew to wrest from the ocean bottom the five million dollars in gold and silver in the strongroom of the Peninsular and Oriental steamer *Egypt*.

"Will you tell us the salvage story of the *Egypt?*" I suggested.

Ricco's face softened into a smile of satisfaction, for he liked nothing better than to tell a tale of the sea. "With pleasure," he replied, and paused while he lighted his pipe. Then spreading his great bulk out on a deck-chair and clasping his hands across his paunch, he began a saga of men in battle with the sea.

I will try to tell in essence the story as he told it:

One fine May morning some twenty years ago the 8000-ton steamer *Egypt* left her London dock bound for Bombay, India. On board were some fifty passengers and a crew of nearly three hundred men and officers. In her strongroom were stored fifteen tons of gold and silver bullion and coins, all valued at about five million dollars. Her schedule called for a stop at Marseilles, where 110 passengers, India-bound, were to join her.

Through the Straits of Dover and the English Channel the *Egypt* was favored with calm seas and a mere zephyr of a breeze. Shortly after she left the Channel Islands on her port hand, however, the horizon was hidden in a gauzy haze that became more opaque with every mile.

About 7 P.M. the vessel had rounded the island of Ushant some twenty-five miles off the French coast. Now a pea-soup fog enshrouded the ship, therefore the captain laid a course across the treacherous Bay of Biscay that would enable him to round Cape Finisterre, Spain, with safety. In this he was following the approved trade route. The fog was so thick that the foredeck of the ship was invisible from the bridge. A confusion of whistles and blasts and toots came from several directions. The *Egypt*, fully conscious of the danger, blew her whistle at the required intervals and held her course at reduced speed. Yet danger did not seem imminent since the other vessels following the trade route were on courses parallel to the *Egypt*'s and so the lookouts kept their watchfulness concentrated dead ahead. The fog grew thicker till visibility was zero.

About sundown the blast of a ship's whistle was heard off the port bow. It seemed to be nearer than the others. When it was repeated, it was off the *Egypt*'s beam but it caused no anxiety, the captain reasoning that he was passing the invisible vessel.

The next moment a ship's bow loomed eerily through the fog. There was an instant of horror and then a rending crash as the stem of the intruder ripped through the *Egypt*'s plates as if they had been so much muslin. Both ships shuddered under the impact and then parted till neither could see the other in the smothering murk.

A hole as wide as a barn door gaped in the *Egypt*'s side. As the sea rushed in, she listed so heavily that her boats could not be lowered from the davits. Passengers and crew donned life jackets and leaped overboard; they were soon lost in the fog.

The ship that struck the fatal blow proved to be the steamship *Seine*, once an icebreaker. She probed through the fog in search of the foundering vessel. Attracted by the frantic cries of the victims in the water, she lowered every available lifeboat. The work of rescue began. Two hundred thirty of the passengers and crew and several who had died were picked up. Ninety-six were never found.

Hazily through the thinning fog the *Egypt* was discovered lying on her side with her stern partially submerged. In exactly twenty minutes from the moment of the crash the stricken ship slipped quietly under the surface, leaving only a vanishing patch of foam to mark her resting place.

Before this, however, every effort was made to report the ship's position. Immediately after the crash the radio operator on the *Egypt* began sending out the official call for assistance. During the twenty minutes the vessel remained afloat, his instrument chattered incessantly with the dreaded SOS and his report of the vessel's situation. Radio direction finders on shore took bearings on his signal but they gave only a rough approximation of the position of the sinking vessel. It was reasonably certain she lay somewhere within a quadrangle of twenty-five square miles and about thirty miles from shore.

With such scant information the search for the *Egypt* became a classic example of hunting for a needle in a haystack. Several salvage companies tried and failed, but others continued the search, buoyed by the hope of recovering the treasure that was of far greater value than the ship herself.

There were many opinions on the exact location of the wreck; no two of them agreed. A spot on a chart is easy to find but finding that exact spot on the open sea is a different story. Lucky indeed would be the captain of a vessel who, after a run of thirty miles from shore, would be able to come closer than a mile from the desired spot.

Nearly seven years had gone by since the sinking of the *Egypt*. Despite the many attempts to recover the treasure, it still rested hidden securely. Only once during that period was there even a faint hope of success. That was when a diver reported a large vessel resembling the *Egypt* lying on the bottom. A violent storm put an end to further operations. When the weather permitted a renewal of the work, no trace of the wreck was found during weeks of strenuous search.

After all efforts had failed and the treasure hunters had given up their sleuthing as hopeless, an Italian salvage company took over. Known internationally, SORIMA (*Societá Recuperi Maritimi*) had a record of phenomenal success in recovering many millions in treasure from sunken ships.

The salvage vessel *Artiglio* was assigned to the operation. As ships go, she was not large—less than 500 tons—but what she lacked in size she made up in quality and quantity of equipment. In her divers' room, forbidden to crew members, the most advanced models of diving gear and the tools necessary for their maintenance were hung on walls and brackets. There were two Neufeldt and Kuhnke diving shells, mammoth affairs, each weighing nearly a thousand pounds. Made of cast steel, they were capable of resisting pressure at a depth of 600 feet. Here too was a mysterious cylindrical object. It resembled a giant fire-hydrant nearly eight feet tall and as big around as an oil drum. On its dome were circular windows that stared like the eyes of a startled owl. It was an observation shell, known aboard the ship as the EYE. The diver encased in it acted merely as an observer. From foredeck to fantail the ship was cluttered with an endless variety of salvage equipment.

Accompanied by the salvage vessel *Rostro*, the *Artiglio* put out from Brest for the general area in which the *Egypt* was known to have disappeared. The scene of the wreck had been reported from three sources. All of them disagreed on the latitude but they agreed on the longitude—5°, 29′ West. The most logical course for the salvagers to follow was to sweep the bottom along the line of longitude.

Now sweeping is a slow and tedious process. Having moored a buoy marking the start, the *Artiglio* passed the end of a wire cable, called a sweep, to the *Rostro*. The ships then parted company, moving in opposite directions until they were half a mile apart and nearly a mile of the wire sweep lay on the bottom between them. In answer to a signal from the *Artiglio's* whistle, both vessels moved in the same direction, dragging the sweep along the bottom.

The sea was calm, the weather was clear and the ships progressed at a snail's pace, hour after hour plodding their parallel courses. About mid-afternoon the wire sweep became caught in an obstruction and stiffened taut as a steel bar. The engine telegraphs on both ships sounded full astern so as to ease the tremendous strain. Hours of maneuvering to free the wire passed without success.

Meantime hearts beat a little faster and hopes ran a little higher. Perhaps the obstruction that snagged the sweep was the treasure ship, *Egypt,* herself! The salvage officer on the *Artiglio* decided to send down a diver to determine what was holding the wire sweep in its grip. A diving shell was readied and with a diver encased within it, was hoisted from the hold and lowered over the side. Despite its half-ton weight, a swiftly flooding tide whisked away the shell and its occupant as if it were bait on the end of a line and held it in suspension high above the bottom. A maneuver of the *Artiglio* so that she too drifted with the tide, enabled the diver to sink to the ocean floor. Swept slowly along by the relentless current, he was suddenly confronted by a forty foot pinnacle rock with the wire sweep clamped firmly in a cleft in such a way it could be freed only by a vertical lift.

With darkness approaching and a fresh breeze now roughing up the sea, the outlook was disturbing. The *Artiglio's* windlass began spooling in the cable on its huge drum. The diver was hoisted on board and the vessel crept stern-first to a position immediately above the rock. The fathometer showed a depth of 410 feet. Suddenly the strain on the wire sweep eased and in a moment it was free.

Again the ships took their respective positions and again the sweeping operation began. It was a night of torment. By midnight the wind had increased to half-gale force and from a direction opposed to that of a swiftly ebbing tide. As a result, huge crested seas belabored both vessels mercilessly. Then as if to make matters more difficult, the sweep became snagged on rocks again and again until the strain and grinding friction severed the wire.

The frayed ends were spliced on board the *Artiglio* and again the ships on their parallel courses continued their sweeping. Now, however, the wire was raised so it was higher than the rocks but deep enough to catch the tall masts or the stacks

of the *Egypt*. This was accomplished by lowering an anchor
weighing several tons from each of the ships to a depth halfway between the surface and the bottom. The wire sweep
was secured to the anchors so that it extended from vessel to
vessel in a manner not unlike a cable on a suspension bridge.
In spite of this ingenious device, several obstructions were
brushed by the lifted sweep. Those occasions were a signal
to heave to while a diver in a diving shell was lowered to investigate. Several wrecks were found all battered and torn
by the violent action of the sea. None of them was the cov-
eted *Egypt*.

And so the *Artiglio* and the *Rostro* pursued their quest for
a month or more. They plodded back and forth over their
ten-mile courses, each course adjoining its neighbor. Occasionally to make the search more thorough, they varied the
sweeping technique. The *Rostro* acted as a pivot while the
Artiglio circled around her with half a mile of the wire sweeping the bottom in a mile-wide circle. The vicious weather for
which the Bay of Biscay is noted often interrupted operations,
forcing the ships to run to cover in the harbor at Brest.

Winter came and with it the cessation of sweeping. The
five-million-dollar prize still lay deep down under. In port,
word of the treasure quest spread rapidly. Clairvoyants, nec-
romancers and pseudo-scientists bombarded the salvage officer
of the *Artiglio* with guarantees that their psychic powers gave
them knowledge of the exact location of the treasure ship.
All of them made a certain condition: they were to receive
ten percent of the recovered riches.

One, a Franciscan monk, caught the attention of the *Artiglio*'s salvage officer. He was a mere wisp of a man, advanced
in years but with a glitter of youth in his eyes. When he
came on board the *Artiglio*, he carried a handful of willow
twigs. His brown cassock hung loosely on his slender frame,

his sandaled feet moved on the gear-cluttered deck with the sureness of a cat. He spoke Italian like a native although French was his mother tongue. Before he was an hour on board he was on friendly terms with the ship's personnel; they called him "Padre."

With a certain modesty he stated that since boyhood he had been endowed with a power he could not explain. In the presence of gold a strange sensation, as from a mild electric current, darted from his elbows to his finger-tips. During a visit to the United States while he was still a young man, he saw a professional "dowser" discover water and minerals in the earth with the aid of a witch-hazel twig. On his return to France he experimented with twigs of many kinds and found that a willow twig, held sharply bowed in his hands, acted as a divining rod when he approached gold.

The salvage officer, a hard-headed hard-fisted man with little use for fantasy, had accepted the friar's story in all good faith. He too had been in the United States and had often heard of the divining rod as a means of discovering mineral substances hidden in the earth. His faith was strengthened when the Padre approached him with a bowed twig in his hands and made several undulating passes like a stage hypnotist. Each time the twig passed close to the officer's chest, it seemed to tremble slightly. "You have gold on you," the friar whispered.

There was a look of surprise on the officer's face as he threw open the collar of his heavy woolen shirt and exposed a small religious medal of gold suspended from his neck by a thin golden chain.

A member of the crew, a cynical unbeliever, stepped up and challenged the monk to find gold on him. Smilingly the man in the cassock nodded assent and passed the bent twig several times close to the sailor's face. With each passing the twig trembled slightly. "There's gold in your mouth," the friar said. And the sailor gasped, no longer an unbeliever. Three of his molars were capped with gold.

When the *Artiglio* resumed sweeping operations, the Padre, while not on the payroll, was considered by all hands as one of the ship's family. As the salvage ship plodded back and forth over the area in which the treasure was supposed to lie, the Padre, his cassock girded up around his waist, leaned over the rail on the foredeck hour after hour with twig in hands and an occasional prayer on his pinched lips. Once when the sweep line snagged on what was possibly a wreck, he gave a solemn blessing to the diver and his shell as they were hoisted over the side. In the days following, as frequent dives were made in unusually deep water, the good man seemed more concerned with the safety of the soul within the shell than in the prospect of great riches. Indeed on such occasions the willow twigs were laid aside.

As the summer progressed, violent storms often sent the salvage ships back to the sanctuary of Brest Harbor. It was during one of those interludes that the little monk left the ship for a stroll along the waterfront. While going down the gangway he paused and turning toward the vessel, raised a hand in benediction, then walked slowly away. He was never seen again.

Two days later a bearded man, describing himself as an occult scientist, boarded the *Artiglio*. He had with him an instrument in a black carrying case that he insisted would point in the direction of precious metals just as the mariner's compass points to the magnetic north. A student of the black art of necromancy, he talked at length of his success as a finder of lost and valuable objects. He was suave and persuasive, a super salesman. The captain of the *Artiglio* and the salvage officer, simple seafaring men, were carried away by the pseudo-scientific arguments of "Monsieur le Professeur," as he styled himself, and particularly by his offer to carry on his exploration for a modest fee, a small share of the *Egypt*'s gold.

During a lull in the conversation, the captain blurted, "Well, nothing venture, nothing gain. Let's give him a chance to prove himself."

"Agreed," replied the salvage officer.

But there was a hitch. Monsieur le Professeur, subject to sea-sickness, insisted that his observations be made from land. The following morning the three men drove in an antiquated automobile to the little village of Matineau situated on a headland overlooking the general area of the sea where the *Egypt* lay hidden. Monsieur le Professeur set up his apparatus with scrupulous care and swept the calm sea through an eye-piece. The instrument, however, pointed its needle not seaward but landward. Disgusted and infuriated, the captain and salvage officer hurried back to their ship, leaving the professor with his fake scientific contraption to get back to Brest the best way he could.

The weather had cleared. The *Artiglio* and the *Rostro* put out again to continue their marine game of hide and seek. The sky, washed by the recent storm, was cloudless. A westerly breeze rippled the sea. A few gulls, following the ship, soared on motionless wings. The *Artiglio*'s salvage officer, deep in thought, paced the deck in the lee of the superstructure. On the bridge the captain scanned the sea ahead. "Steady as she goes," he muttered to the helmsman. "Number two buoy lies dead ahead." He pulled the whistle rope to signal the *Rostro* to come alongside. On deck preparations were made to pass the end of the sweep from ship to ship.

The buoy was picked up and hoisted to the *Artiglio*'s deck.

It had been placed before running to Brest to mark the spot where the search would be resumed. With the sweep secured, the ships veered away from each other until they were half a mile apart. Then they squared away on their parallel courses. The wind began to freshen, kicking up a moderate sea. The ships had made scarcely half a mile when the sweep became snagged on the bottom. All attempts to free it failed. The heavy duty winches on both ships reeled in on the sweep until the wire was stiff and rose almost vertically from the bottom.

The salvage officer laid his ear on the cable where it passed over the stern. He could hear the crunching of metal on metal 400 feet down. It was certain now that the wire held fast, not on a rock but in the wreckage of a steel ship. He ordered one of the divers, Gildo, to prepare to go down to investigate. All three diving shells were held in readiness.

In a few minutes Gildo, encased in half a ton of cast steel, was lowered over the side. As he blew his air ballast and began to sink, he was caught in the grip of an ebbing tide and was carried far astern. And there he hung, some fifty feet under the surface with 350 feet of water below him. Because of the rushing tide, diving was out of the question. Only brute force would free the sweep or part it.

The steam winches spluttered and strained, thus forcing the sterns of the salvage ships lower in the water and permitting the swelling seas to tumble in on the afterdecks, washing men and gear into the scuppers.

The prospect of having located the *Egypt* instilled bulldog tenacity in the men. In the snare of the sweep, riches might well await every man on board. They would hang on to the wreck in spite of rip-roaring tides and boarding seas and in spite of the storm that was threatening.

It was two hours to the turn of the tide and slack water when a diver could go down to identify the wreck. Whether the wire could stand the strain was a question none could answer. The wind was freshening and the seas were now showing white fangs of foam.

While the salvage officer on the *Artiglio* was debating the advisability of relieving the strain on the wire, the ship was rushed by an unusually high sea. With her stern held captive, she could not rise to it. She quivered down her entire length as hundreds of tons of water tumbled on board. Straining under the tremendous lift of the sea, the wire came to the end of its endurance. It quivered in crunching spasms as strand after strand broke loose. Then with a convulsive whoosh, twenty feet of it snaked out of the water and fell back limp as a wet sock.

To the optimists on board who believed that their months of heartbreaking toil had been rewarded at last, the parting of the cable was stark tragedy.

In spite of worsening weather the captain ordered a boat lowered. Its expert crew labored for hours, dragging the bottom with grappling irons, but wind and tide soon carried the ship and boat far from the area where the supposed treasure ship had been located. Although the latitude and longitude of the wreck had been reasonably established, it was never found again.

When the ends of the sweep were taken aboard ship and subjected to close examination, iron rust and flecks of white paint were plainly visible on the fractured strands of wire. This gave the doubting Thomases, who insisted the *Egypt* lay farther to the south, a moment of elation, since the treasure ship, like all vessels of the Peninsular and Oriental Steamship Line, had her hull painted black and her superstructure and stacks a tawny buff.

Violent weather paroxysms now drove the salvage ships to cover at Brest. No sooner had the vessels been tied up at their piers than they were again beset by soothsayers, fortune tellers, palm readers and crackpots, all fanatically bent on making easy money. The captains and salvage officers would have none of them. They were shoved ashore the moment they boarded the ships.

Months of dreary and often dangerous sweeping followed. Each turn of the tide or phase of the moon or shift in the wind brought new hope of generous financial reward. For in many salvage operations, as in this case, members of the crew shared in the spoils.

The work was hampered seriously by overpowering currents that prevented the divers from reaching the bottom or endangered their lives while attempting to survey a wreck.

Once the master diver himself was trapped in an old wreck that had snagged the sweep. On that day diving conditions appeared good on the surface. The sea was calm, the sky clear and the tide was in the stage of slack water. Using the ponderous observation shell, he had descended almost vertically some 300 feet when without his knowledge he was caught in the grip of one of those mysterious sub-surface currents. Since there is no sense of motion inside the shell unless some object is seen to pass by, the diver was unaware of his danger. Suddenly he caught a shadowy glimpse of what appeared to be the mast of a sunken ship passing the window of his shell. Then came a metallic scraping on the other side. He knew then he was in trouble. He had been swept between the mast and the steel shrouds that supported it and become trapped in a tangle of gear hanging from the crosstrees at the masthead high above the deck.

He phoned his tender, ordering that the braided line attached to the shell be slacked away, hoping that the current and gravity would free him. A kinked wire shroud hanging empty inches from his window and a constant scraping on the outside of his shell told him he was held fast in a snarl of wire rigging that had been torn loose from its fastenings. Then followed every trick known to the salvager for releasing a diver trapped 300 feet down. Imprisoned in his steel cylinder, the diver was powerless to aid in the effort to free him.

An hour passed and annoyance on the ship was giving way to anxiety. The salvage officer on the *Artiglio* decided to send another diver down to assist in the rescue. Although it was a risky project, the divers on board vied for the privilege of releasing their boss. An articulated shell was used. It allowed the diver considerable freedom of his arms and legs and of the clawlike pincers on the ends of the arm casings.

Following a heavily weighted line from the *Artiglio* to the wreck, the diver despite the current, reached the foredeck of the sunken ship. With three-way telephone communication established between the two divers and the tender on board the salvage vessel, he had little trouble in locating the snared shell. A wire shroud was fouled in the shackle on top of its dome. Another wire in a large loop had snagged the shell halfway up its length.

Even while the rescue diver was at work, the current seemed to lose its force gradually, until it was almost imperceptible. Its strange behavior was doubtless due to the turning of the tide and it proved to be a stroke of luck for rescuer and rescued. When clear of the tangled gear, the signal to hoist was given and finally both shells were in their brackets on the *Artiglio* and the men none the worse for their experience . . . The knowledge of the exact location of the wreck—an old coal carrier—made freeing the sweep an easy task. A charge of dynamite was lowered to the foredeck of the hulk and exploded. The sweep was freed. And the salvage ships continued their seemingly fruitless search for the *Egypt* and her hoard of gold and silver.

Another winter of atrocious weather passed while the *Artiglio* and *Rostro* lay snugly in Brest harbor. The treacherous Bay of Biscay continued to take its toll; many wrecks were reported. It was estimated that over the year the salvage vessels averaged the equivalent of a week's work a month. Tides, currents, fog and storms lasting for days made sweeping perilous and diving impossible. Spring came with warm sunshine and calm seas. Spirits rose and a new determination to find the *Egypt* gripped the men.

The salvage officer pored over the chart which showed the location and extent of every sweeping made and the position of the worthless wrecks that had been found. Only a small portion of the area in which the treasure ship was known to lie had been left uncombed. All searching operations now would be confined to less than a square mile of sea bottom. The officer felt certain that the prize, after a search of nearly two years, would be found there.

Just before the *Artiglio* sailed, the insurance underwriters radioed the ship they were sending on board a professor of electrical engineering from a well-known English technical college. He was the inventor of an electrical device, a kind of galvanometer that would detect the presence of metals lying on the ocean floor. The salvage officer threw up his hands. Here was another crackpot! Sponsored by the underwriters, however, the professor received due consideration but little encouragement. Actually he *was* a man of science; the complex and delicate instrument he brought with him proved to have the power of reacting to *known* wrecks on the bottom. Finding the *Egypt* was another story.

One day the fragile electrodes of the instrument became snagged in a wreck and were injured beyond repair. The professor and his invention were hurried ashore at Brest. Again

vicious weather held the *Artiglio* in her dock for more than a
week. As she was about to cast off in order to continue the
search, a broad-shouldered man came on board and presented
his credentials to the captain and salvage officer. He was none
other than the master of the ship that had sunk the *Egypt*.
He of all people should know where the collision occurred. He
too was employed by the underwriters to assist in the search.

The salvage officer bristled. He had had enough of gratu-
itous advice. He would continue to probe the bottom with
his sweep until every inch of the uncombed area had been
dragged.

One morning shortly after daybreak the sweep wire grew
taut and resisted all efforts to free it. The boss diver, usually
a placid fellow, climbed hurriedly into the tubular observation
shell and was lowered overside. From 400 feet down he reported fair visibility. Soon a black mass loomed up before
him. Even in the dim light he could see quite clearly, as he
was being raised and lowered, row on row of rivets studding
the plates of a large ship.

A hectic hour for the winch-man and tender followed as
the diver ordered his position changed from minute to minute
to bring him within seeing distance of some object or detail
of construction he was familiar with after long study of the
plans and scale model of the *Egypt*. "Up!" "Down!"
"Right!" "Left!" "Fore!" "Aft!" Each order came over the
phone like the crack of a pistol. Finally the command "Hoist
away!" coming up from the deeps set the diving winch buz-
zing. Minutes later the diver clambered from his shell to the
deck. Without a word he hurried to the chartroom for further study of the *Egypt's* plans. All hands noticed that the
diver, usually cool as an ice cube, was flushed with excitement
that soon became contagious to the crew. However, after

several years of frustration and disappointment, none dared express his conviction that at last success had come.

Half a dozen dives were made that afternoon with the purpose of checking and double-checking the identifying details as shown in the plans—number and position of boat davits, windlasses, anchors, scuttles, hatches and deck fittings. That evening an announcement was made to the crew. The wreck on which they had been working was identified beyond all doubt. It was the *Egypt*.

A full moon hung low against a sky of midnight blue. A gentle swell from some far distant storm gave the *Artiglio* a soothing roll. From the foredeck the strumming of a guitar and snatches of lusty song were wafted out over the shimmering sea. The long search ended, the recovery of the treasure was merely a routine job made easier by the fact that the *Egypt* lay on an even keel, just as if she had been afloat.

Shortly after dawn the *Artiglio*'s deck was a scene of bustling activity. Heavily anchored buoys were placed to mark the exact position of the wreck. A varied collection of salvage equipment—grabs, dredges, hooks and heavy hoisting gear— was laid out on the foredeck ready for instant use. The boss diver, having checked critically the observation shell, climbed in. The huge lid was bolted in place and all was ready for the second act of the drama—the recovery of the treasure.

With air ballast blown on entering the water, the shell sank with the speed of an express elevator. It landed on the wreck and squarely on the roof of the captain's cabin. It was a fortunate landing! "Send down number two hook!" the diver phoned his tender.

Within minutes a great white hook came down and stopped a few inches from the front porthole or window of the shell. Then followed sharp instructions by phone from diver to tender. "Six feet to starboard!" "Forward a little. So!"

"Lower away!" "Hold it!" "Hoist! easy does it!" The hook, obedient to the diver's orders, probed around until it caught in the projecting eave of the cabin roof. "Hold it!" "Swing me clear!" The shell and its occupant were whisked some thirty feet to safety. "Okay. Hoist away!" The wooden roof of the cabin, half rotten from seven years' submersion, was torn from its supporting walls and rose as a black shadow less than an oar's length from the diver as it was carried to a distance and deposited on the bottom.

The removal of the roof left the captain's cabin easy of access. The safe containing documents that established the legal identity of the ship, would be found in the captain's personal quarters. Obedient to the diver's phoned orders, he was lifted and lowered into what was once the home of a gallant sailor who, according to tradition, went down with his ship. A floodlight was lowered. In its hazy glare the safe stood out like a tombstone in moonlight.

"Send down the heavy grab!" the diver bellowed into the phone. Soon a lobster claw of steel came down from above. As tall as a man, its giant jaws opened wide to grasp its load. The greater the weight, the tighter was its grip. Complying with the clipped commands of the diver, its mandibles bit into the steel safe and speeded it to the deck of the *Artiglio*. Examination of its contents proved beyond doubt the identity of the *Egypt*, a most important factor in the deliberations of the Admiralty Courts that usually follow on the heels of a salvage operation.

While the safe was being hoisted, the diver waited patiently until he could give the signal to be lifted to the surface. As he peered through the shell window out into the greenish void, he was startled to see a coil of the braided wire that was his lifeline sink slowly until it disappeared in the murky shadows. He phoned his tender to find out what was wrong. The tender with alarm in his voice told him that they had been reeling in his line but it was without weight.

There seemed to be but one explanation: the braided wire had parted. The observation shell was fitted with a heavy metal disk known as a "plate anchor." It was attached to the bottom of the shell and connected by a thin wire cable to a small winch close to the diver's hand. It was intended to give the shell stability and a certain amount of vertical mobility when the wire was paid out from the little winch.

He had no serious misgivings because he knew he could cast off the anchor wire and the shell would rise to the surface by the buoyancy he could create by releasing compressed air from the air cylinder in the shell. He spun the winch wheel that should release him, but after a few turns found it jammed. He realized then that he was a prisoner 400 feet down without even a slim chance for escape.

The salvage officer took over the phone from the tender and gave the diver suggestions and instructions born of long experience with the perils of diving. They all proved futile. Having done everything possible to effect his escape, the diver reconciled himself to the end when his air and oxygen supply gave out. He stared vacantly through the window, his face chalk white. The minutes were running out.

Then as in a dream he saw the light get a little brighter. A wisp of sea-grass appeared and then disappeared *downward*. Two tiny fish stared at him and they too dropped *down* out of sight. A tiny transparent eel-like creature sank below the level of his vision. The light had changed from a greenish dusk to an emerald tint. "*I'm rising!*" he shouted into the phone. "*I'm rising!!*"

A wave of excitement swept the *Artiglio*. None could fathom the strange predicament of the boss diver. The telephone cable that connected the shell with the ship would not stand the strain of hoisting. Boats were lowered and men waited anxiously the surfacing of the shell. It might be injured and sink again as a result of leakage. Several minutes later when it broke the surface 200 feet off the port bow of the salvage ship, it floated at an angle, with half its length submerged.

When it was hoisted on deck, it was discovered that the heavy plate anchor at its base had broken loose. So the mystery was solved. Relieved of the weight of its plate anchor, the shell began to rise. Without any sense of motion the diver was unaware he was being carried upward. When he saw the slack of his cable drop down in front of his window, he assumed the wire had parted. Not until he had seen other objects in what seemed to be downward motion did he realize that he was rising slowly.

Although pale and a bit shaken by his strange experience, he resumed supervision of the preparations for removing the treasure.

The strong-room on the *Egypt* was constructed so that it was possible to lift it and its contents on to the deck of the *Artiglio*, provided sufficient skill and mechanical power were available. Such a method of salvage would mean a considerable saving of labor and expense, also a more complete recovery of the treasure. After a long period of deliberation by officers and divers, it was decided to follow this daring plan.

As the venturesome task was about to begin, Fate stepped in and interrupted the scene. And so began the final act in a drama that was to end in tragedy.

Just when everything was in readiness to raise the strong-room and its content in a single operation, a storm of unusual violence forced the *Artiglio* to run for shelter in Brest harbor.

For several days she snuggled close to her pier while most of her crew, boisterous as boys out of school, enjoyed the pleasures of shore life.

When the wind and sea had lost their venom and the *Artiglio* was about to cast off and return to her job, a radio message from the salvage company upset all perfected plans for the recovery of the gold and silver hoard. Some thirteen years previously a steamship loaded with several thousand tons of ammunition had been sunk in the approach to the harbor of St. Nazaire and had now become a menace to navigation due to a shifting of the channel. Ship and cargo must be demolished without delay.

Only the most expert of salvagers, such as the crew of the *Artiglio*, would be entrusted with such a hazardous undertaking. No one, not even an army expert, could appraise the danger of explosives submerged for thirteen years. Neither would they claim it was without catastrophic possibilities.

With winter approaching the demolition work would have to be done quickly before the bad weather set in. Having taken supplies and necessary wrecking gear on board, the *Artiglio* hurried to where the derelict lay in some sixty feet of water. Wearing the conventional rubberized diving dress, the boss diver went down to make a survey and to determine the best way to demolish the wreck. Despite the long period it had lain under water, the vessel's hull and superstructure appeared sound. Explosives then would be the quickest and most practical method for dismembering the menace.

Immediately they began the work of tearing to shreds a 9000-ton wreck. Charges of dynamite were placed at critical points along the bilge. They were connected so that they would explode simultaneously. An electric wire was led from the train of explosives to the *Artiglio*'s bridge where the boss diver would throw the switch.

Uncertain of what the effect of the explosion would be, the salvage ship withdrew to a distance of nearly two miles, paying out the electric wire as it went. When the signal "All clear" was given, the switch was thrown. Two rows of huge blisters welled up on the surface above the wreck. Geysers shot skyward for a hundred feet and then settled back on the water to be lost in a layer of writhing smoke. After a silence of several seconds a muffled rumble as of distant thunder rolled in on the salvage ship.

Back on location, several divers went down to learn the effect of the blast. They reported a series of holes blown in the hull, none of them larger than an ordinary doorway.

The operation was repeated again and again with ever increasing quantities of dynamite. Before each blast the *Artiglio* retreated to a safe but shorter distance. The moment the "shot" had been fired, the ship returned to its position where inspection by divers revealed that, while the hull of the derelict had been generously punctured, it was still far from complete destruction.

The cobalt blue of the sky had tarnished with a murky haze. The sea, losing its sparkle, was turning gray and wrinkled. The razor edge of the horizon was lost behind a misty veil hanging low between sea and sky. Bad weather was brewing.

"We're in for a blow that will drive us to shelter," the boss diver said. "We've still a few hours and about five hundred pounds of dynamite that we can place and shoot before the storm breaks. Number three hold is loaded to the hatches with high explosive shells. That's where we attack!"

An hour and a half later a low wall of dynamite sticks had been built under the bilge of the wreck and connected by an electric cable to the salvage ship.

Everything now was in readiness for the big bang. The

Artiglio cast off her mooring and moved away cautiously, paying out the wire as she went. On the bridge the boss diver, the salvage officer and the captain agreed that to retire to the usual distance would consume too much time. The ship now had a pitch and roll that, though slight, would endanger the slender electric wire.

When 300 yards from the wreck, the boss diver signaled "Stop!" With the heartbeat of the engine stilled, only the whistling and moaning of the ever rising wind disturbed the silence on the bridge.

The boss diver stood with hand poised over the switch that would set off the blast. The salvage officer, doubt on his face, whispered, "Are you sure we're far enough away?"

The diver did not reply. His fingers closed on the switch handle and after a moment's hesitation, threw it upward and into contact. Before he could release it, several acres of the sea around the wreck welled up in a huge green blister that instantly exploded, sending a pillar of smoke and water large as a city block a thousand feet into the air, thus forming an empty crater in the sea hundreds of yards in diameter.

A giant wave, propelled by the explosion, rushed out in all directions, almost overwhelming the *Artiglio*. Before she could recover from the shock, the water, seeking its level, rushed back with devastating force to fill the crater. The salvage ship was caught like a leaf in a mill-race. With her decks submerged, water cascaded through her open hatches and in less than a minute after the switch had been thrown, the gallant *Artiglio*, heroic survivor of many battles with the sea, lay on the bottom, a twisted and broken hulk. Only the half-dozen men who were on deck, were picked up more dead than alive. The rest of the ship's company of some twenty men were lost.

The "Big Bang," prepared by the boss diver, was bigger than he had anticipated. The unpredictable dynamite had set off the thousands of tons of ammunition that had lain for thirteen years in the hold of the wreck. The blast was heard all over the seven seas, wherever salvage men work deep down under.

Raising the contents of the *Egypt's* strong-room was a routine operation that could be performed by any well equipped salvage vessel and crew. It was indeed an anticlimax to the years of heartbreak and hardship bravely borne by the men on the *Artiglio* in their search for a treasure-laden ship that had been given up as lost forever.

It was dark that evening when my friend the diver and I boarded the launch to return to Barranquilla. When we were about in mid-stream, he remarked, "It seems strange that Ricco never once mentioned the fact that the boss diver lost on the *Artiglio* was his twin brother."

7   HIDDEN TREASURE

For centuries men, driven by a lust for gold, have probed land and sea for treasure hoards lost or hidden. Even today great sums are being spent on expeditions for the recovery of chests bursting with gold, caskets of jewels, leather bags of coins— moidores, doubloons, ducats and pieces of eight—reported to be buried in the hulks of ships sunk in battle or storm hundreds of years ago.

It is difficult to account for the strange seizures that impel otherwise normal people into those visionary projects. I once knew a lawyer, a staid practical New Englander and a hard-shell conservative. Among his clients was a contractor who had met with financial reverses and who found himself unable to pay my friend the lawyer a substantial sum for legal services.

One morning this client appeared at the lawyer's office, carrying a large manilla envelope that he seemed to guard carefully. "I've come to clear up my indebtedness," he said, "and to show my appreciation for the many kindnesses you've shown me." He drew from the envelope a map crudely drawn on parchment and yellowed with age. Spreading it out on the desk, he pointed to a spot marked X, close to tiny Raccoon Island in the Bahamas. "Right there," he said, "a fortune in gold lies buried in a ship that sank about a hundred and twenty years ago. This map was drawn by the mate, one of two survivors. It was given to me by a native of Guantanamo, Cuba, whose family had owned it for many years. It was a kind of reward for having saved his only son from drowning.

"I visited Raccoon Island," he continued, "and sure enough, a hundred and fifty yards off shore I found the wreck, or what was left of it, in thirty feet of water. Always a good swimmer and diver, I probed the sand and mud along the rotted keel of the ship. In less than an hour I found these." He drew from his pocket two gold coins, Spanish doubloons, and laid them on the map.

The lawyer's eyes gleamed as he fondled the coins between his lean fingers. "But why didn't you recover more of these?" he asked shrewdly.

"I returned at once to the States to secure proper diving equipment and a diver I could trust," he answered. "It would cost only a few thousand dollars, but the stake was large. Al-

ready the great depression had set in, and in less than a fort-
night I found myself penniless as did tens of thousands of
others who were caught in the ruins of the stock market. My
contracting business fell off to just a few odd jobs. I've lost
all interest in the sunken treasure and so I've decided to turn
it over to you. I will sign an agreement to that effect."

The lawyer approved; the necessary papers were drawn up
and executed.

Soon it was noticed by both family and friends that the
staid and meticulous lawyer began to have dreamy spells in
which, for hours at a time, he studied the map, now his cher-
ished possession. He visited the local library and borrowed
all available books dealing with the Bahamas and the Bahama
Channel north of Haiti and Cuba. Among his law books
were interspersed treatises on pirates, freebooters and buccan-
eers. He often harangued with friends on the fabulous for-
tunes that lay on the bottom of the seas over which the
cut-throats roamed in search of plunder.

Treasure trove and the laws governing it became an obses-
sion with him. Once when a favorite nephew, a promising
young engineer, was visiting him, he took from his safe the
ancient map and eloquently, as if pleading before a jury, plied
the young man with borrowed facts and figures and data relat-
ing to the vast wealth that lay unclaimed on the ocean floor.
Filled with the spirit of adventure that always has been the
heritage of youth, Harvey, the nephew, was carried away by
his uncle's powers of persuasion.

A month later an expedition left Boston for Raccoon Cay
on a chartered trawler with all equipment necessary for the
recovery of the golden hoard. It was the hurricane season.
The trawler was anchored well off the tiny islet while a comfortable camp was built in a nearby sheltered cove.

Two days of searching were rewarded by finding the sunken ship. Alfredo, a diver hailing from Havana and something of an autocrat, took charge of the salvage operation. Before signing on for the expedition, he insisted on taking along his own tender, a morose Costa Rican who had worked with him for years. The trawler's power-boat was used as the diving launch.

On the morning the diving was about to begin Harvey stood on the beach, looking thoughtfully at the inscrutable sea. Members of the crew were busy with their various duties. Alfredo sat stolidly on a crate while his tender secured his diving dress to the breastplate. A small object, half buried in the sand, caught Harvey's attention. Picking it up, he was overcome with joy. It was a gold coin.

"Alfredo!" he shouted. "Look!"

The diver fingered the coin and frowned. "It's bad news," he said.

Piqued and disappointed, Harvey snapped, "What do you mean—'bad news?' "

The diver was silent for a moment, and then retorted with a touch of spleen, "I mean the gold is scattered over many acres of bottom. Most of it is buried in the sand."

"But," replied Harvey, "gold does not float away like chips of wood."

With annoyance in his tone Alfredo growled, "As an engineer, you must know that the weight of gold or silver or even the human body when in water, is but a small fraction of its weight on dry land. When caught in the underwater surge of storm waves, coins and even heavier objects are swept along like snowflakes in a gale."

The weather was propitious for the first dive. With scarcely a ripple on the surface the diver was faintly visible against the white sand on the bottom as he prowled ape-fashion among the rusted ribs of the ancient ship. Occasionally he was seen to stop and pick up some object which he placed in the wire mesh basket he carried.

In an hour or so he came up for a breather. As he hung on to the ladder from the side of the launch, he raised the basket. It contained a number of coins, dingy and tarnished, but unmistakably *gold*. The men on deck gave little yelps of delight.

After the diver's helmet had been lifted from the breastplate, his sweaty face was wrinkled in disgust. "It's going to be slow work," he grunted. "The stuff is scattered all over the place!"

During the days that followed the reward was slim. Each gold piece recovered was grubbed by hand from the sand and silt of the bottom. Gloom had begun to settle over the little band of treasure seekers. Failure seemed inevitable. Only a faint spark of hope and the physical evidence of the presence of gold kept the men at their daily drudgery.

One evening while Harvey and Alfredo were discussing the outlook, the diver's face lighted up. "There's still a chance," he said cheerfully. "We'll see tomorrow."

The following morning the diver took a shovel down with him and after an unusually short time under water, signaled to be hauled up. As he reached the surface, he raised the metal basket. It was heavy with gold coins.

When his helmet had been removed, he was plied with excited questions as to where and how he found the treasure. A grin of satisfaction rippled across his face as he tapped his forehead with a forefinger. "Just used my brain," he answered and then continued, "Yesterday while probing around near the stern end of the keel, above which must have been the captain's quarters, I found buried in the sand some badly corroded metal fastenings and hinges, evidently from a wooden chest long since rotted away. Then it occurred to me that the chest had contained the gold and that it had been kept in the captain's cabin. If I guessed right, I knew that at least some of the contents had been buried in the sand below and had escaped the underwater violence caused by storms. That's why I took a shovel with me this morning. As I dug into the packed sand, I could feel it crunch against hard substances that I knew were not shellfish. Then I used the wire basket as a sieve. After I'd put the first few shovelfuls into it, I shook it hard. The sand disappeared and there lay what you see before you, more than a hundred Spanish doubloons. And there's plenty more where they came from."

It was a day of joy for all hands as basket after basket of doubloons came up from the bottom. Each of the coins was worth about thirteen silver dollars.

At last fortune had favored the little band of treasure hunters. The future looked bright, the weather was kindly, riches lay within their reach. Again and again Alfredo went down with shovel and basket, leaving a trail of silvery bubbles to mark the spot.

He had been under one day about ten minutes when two triangular dorsal fins sliced the surface once around the diving launch and then disappeared. "Sharks!" the tender bellowed to his comrades and waited the diver's signal to haul up. Presently the lines were almost snatched from his hands by a vicious tug. "Speed her up!" he yelled to the men on the air pump as he hauled in on the lines. Again there was a shocking pull on the lines and a savage shaking as a dog might shake a rat. The air rising from the diver broke the surface, not in bubbles but in swollen blobs.

As the limp form of the diver was lifted into the launch, it was evident he was seriously injured; water seeping from a gaping rent in his diving dress was stained with blood. With his helmet removed, he was hurried on board the trawler where Harvey was checking the ship's supplies. Fortunately Harvey, who had been an Eagle Scout, was proficient in First Aid. The injured man's leg was badly lacerated and bleeding profusely. With antiseptics, tourniquet and bandages from the locker the extensive wounds were staunched. The nearest professional medical aid was in the town of Caibarien, Cuba, 230 miles to the west. Within the hour the trawler was under way.

Twenty-six hours later the trawler pulled into the primitive harbor at Caibarien and tied up at a rickety fishing pier. A local official who had come on board told Harvey there was only one doctor in town, an Americano who lived nearby. The mate hurried ashore and soon returned, leading a disheveled and shaky figure of a man carrying a physician's black bag. Unshaven but otherwise clean, he wore a rusty alpaca coat. In lieu of a belt his baggy trousers were held up by a length of thin rope. His unsocked feet were protected by a pair of shabby sandals.

"I'm Doctor Chadwick," he said in a cultured voice. "A case of shark bite, I believe."

A little nonplussed by the doctor's uncouth appearance, Harvey received him politely and led him where Alfredo was lying on the mate's bunk in a semi-conscious state. The doctor examined the bandaging and tourniquet. "Not bad," he said with an approving nod. "I see you have relieved the tourniquet pressure at proper intervals."

He took from his bag half-a-dozen surgical instruments. "Have these boiled for twenty minutes!" he said with professional briskness. He snipped several wide strips from a roll of gauze and with them covered the top of a sea chest and set several vials of medicaments on the improvised instrument table. Then with the unmistakable air of hospital authority, he said to Harvey, "Please go! I must not be disturbed. Send in the instruments when they are ready."

Harvey obeyed meekly, for under the guise of this human derelict was a skilled practitioner and no mistake. An hour and a half later Dr. Chadwick emerged from the operating room sweating profusely, older and paler than when he had come on board.

"Doctor, how is the patient?" Harvey asked anxiously.

Dr. Chadwick stroked his stubbled chin with a forefinger. "He'll pull through," he said gravely, "but it will be many months before he can dive again."

This verdict put an end to the dreams of wealth that had buoyed the party during the lean days. Without a diver further work was impossible. Harvey hurried to Santa Clara thirty miles away to telegraph the bad news to his uncle and to ask for instructions. A reply came the following morning. It read: "See to it the wounded man is properly cared for. Then return at once."

Alfredo was moved to the doctor's home, a one-story three-roomed house on the waterfront where he received competent medical care. Within a week the doctor declared that, thanks to a strong constitution and indomitable will power, the patient might make the trip to Boston and hospitalization without ill effect, assuming of course he received proper care on board the trawler.

With ample fuel and supplies on board, the staunch little vessel put out on its 1700 mile run to Boston. Favored by a calm sea and clear weather, the trawler logged off the miles with the regularity of a ticking clock. When only a few miles off Cape Cod and only a few hours from her home port, she entered a dense fog bank. On the bridge the engine telegraph rang for half speed. Almost simultaneously the ship shuddered from stem to rudder post and came almost to a dead stop. An avalanche of water came tumbling over the bow as she lurched heavily to port. She had struck a derelict while still running at full speed.

It took those on the bridge but a moment to realize that the ship was fatally wounded, as she was already going down by the head. Her empty fish holds were filling rapidly. Men aroused from their sleep scrambled on deck. There was confusion but no panic.

"Prepare to abandon ship!" came through a megaphone from the bridge. Harvey and the mate rushed to the assistance of the crippled diver and carried him on deck. The number one boat was about to be lowered. The injured man was lifted gently and placed in the stern sheets.

"Lower away!" the mate shouted. The boat was soon hidden in the haze. Number two boat with the remainder of the crew followed.

Fog-blinded, the men swung on their oars in the general direction of the Cape. After several hours of rowing the boat keels crunched on the sandy beach at Race Point. There the castaways were discovered by a Coastguardsman on beach patrol.

At the Coast Guard lifeboat station Harvey related for the record the story of the ill-fated treasure hunt. In the course of his narrative he declared that the expedition had cost to date some $21,000. The value of the sunken trawler was estimated at $80,000 while the recovered gold that went down with it was valued at less than $4,000.

The Chief Petty Officer, who had recorded for the log the essentials of Harvey's story, remarked drily, "Seems to me that was an expensive way to move a pot of gold from the bottom of the sea in the Bahamas to the bottom of the sea off Cape Cod."

The lust for lost treasure, once acquired, is difficult to overcome despite the million-to-one odds against its victims. It seems to be a mania, a kind of psychopathic barrier to reason, logic or plain horse sense. There is no walk of life immune to its virus. Kings have quarreled, barons have battled and lowly beachcombers have haggled over some rotted off-shore hulk that rumor insisted contained a rich hoard. For many years maritime law courts were glutted with legal battles to establish ownership to some ancient wreck reported to contain a fabulous fortune in gold, silver and precious stones. Some of those suits still plague the courts but they have become so snarled in legal technicalities that clear-cut decisions are all but impossible.

A Spanish galleon, the *Florencia,* sunk off the Scottish coast more than 350 years ago, was for generations the cause of open warfare between two powerful Scottish clans. Men fought and died to establish their claim to the $150,000,000 in gold that was reported to have gone down with the ship. Between battles generations of clansmen tried to salvage at least a part of the treasure. A handful of scattered coins, a few silver domestic utensils and the metal sections of a number of ancient firearms were their only reward. A hundred years after the sinking, a diver went down in a primitive diving bell in which he nearly lost his life. He reported several large cannon scattered about in the vicinity of the wreck and that was all.

Another hundred years passed and still the strife and search went on, now with the aid of witchery, sorcery, alchemy, second sight and a host of everyday crackpots, but all without success.

About 1875, a salvage syndicate that had adopted the modern diving dress still in its primitive state, obtained a concession to carry on the search. A dowser of some reputation for discovering lost valuables was employed. Weeks were spent in vain attempts to locate treasure.

In 1903, a Scottish syndicate with the latest diving, dredging and underwater lighting equipment took up the quest. A cannon, a few coins, a few odds and ends of silver were all the divers had to show for their extreme effort.

During the decade that followed more than a dozen attempts were made at considerable cost to recover the *Florencia*'s treasure. The last was by a retired British army colonel who gave his undertaking the modern touch. For nearly a year he conducted an alluring advertising campaign for funds throughout the British Empire.

The Colonel, a shrewd judge of human weaknesses, wielded a seductive pen. While he made no promises, he painted a rosy picture of the great wealth to be gained from a small investment. Money flowed in from most unexpected sources. From members of Parliament, from merchants, laborers and idlers, from castles and hovels the daily mail brought subscriptions by hundreds, all from people intent on getting a lot for a little. The virus of "easy money" had infected the British more seriously than the Colonel had dreamed.

By the time he was ready to begin salvage operations World War I had begun. Treasure was forgotten. The British had their hands full of more serious matters.

At the end of the war the Colonel, true to his promises, led a well equipped expedition to the scene of the lost treasure. Weeks of arduous search passed with no more reward than a handful of gold coins and a collection of ancient arms. Recurrent storms drove the salvage ship to shelter. Each storm piled up another layer of sand and mud around the wreck. Urged by the hard-driving Colonel, two divers worked in spells around the clock. More than ten acres of the bottom was explored foot by foot. Explosives were used close to the wreck. The resultant craters in the bottom failed to reveal more than buried debris. With heavy heart and light purse the Colonel and his crew gave up the quest and returned to the home port.

So thoroughly was the legend of the treasure ship implanted over the years that the search went on despite the failures of past generations.

As late as 1951 a descendant of one of the warring clans, a titled man of wealth, prevailed on the British Navy to send a corps of salvagers with modern equipment to try their luck at finding the golden hoard, then so badly needed for the Empire's exchequer.

In the maritime insurance establishment of Lloyd's of London, there is a spacious and ancient assembly place where ship-owners, ship-masters and mariners in general discuss insurance of ships and cargoes with the seriousness and fervor of brokers on the floor of the Stock Exchange.

Near the center of the place stands a pulpit-like rostrum over which is hung an ornate bell that is tolled to notify those present that a ship reported lost has arrived safely in port. It is known all over the world, wherever shipmen gather, as the "Lutine's Bell," named for the British frigate on which it had been used for nearly a quarter century. The *Lutine*, a 900-ton vessel mounting thirty-two guns, was chosen by the Admiralty to transport gold insured by Lloyd's for more than $5,000,000 to a banking house in Hamburg. That was in 1799.

While off the coast of Holland the *Lutine* was caught in a violent gale and went down with her precious cargo and all hands. The Dutch, at war with England at that time, claimed the lost frigate and began salvage operations without delay. Local fishermen, familiar with the treacheries of the water at the scene of the wreck, were employed. Going down

on weighted lines in the manner of pearl fishers, they succeeded in retrieving a number of the gold ingots. A storm
interrupted their operations. When they returned a few days
later, the divers found the wreck buried under a deep layer
of sand and mud. Each succeeding storm spread an extra
blanket of sea bottom over the hulk. Salvage was abandoned.

Thirteen years later, in 1812, Lloyd's of London who had
insured the lost gold, claimed its ownership when the king of
the Netherlands, impoverished by war and infected with the
goldbug, issued a royal decree entitling a Dutch Company to
sole salvage rights to the cargo of the sunken *Lutine* with the
understanding that the Crown would receive one-half of the
badly needed gold.

Seven years and a fortune spent on salvage work went un-
rewarded. Disgusted, the Dutch Government finally recog-
nized the right of Lloyd's of London to the wreck and its
content and agreed to permit the English company to carry
on salvage operations on a fifty-fifty basis. The result was zero
and again salvaging was discontinued.

Meanwhile natives alongshore, taking advantage of govern-
mental withdrawal, swarmed over the scene of the sinking and
eked out slim reward in occasional coins and odds and ends of
silver and other metal objects. Even teen-age boys and girls
became skilled divers who could stay under water longer and
bring up more loot than their elders. And so, searching the
ocean bed became a local institution that was part game and
part gain.

In 1856, an American trading schooner, seeking shelter from
a gale, let go her anchor several hundred yards north of the
spot where salvagers had sought the *Lutine*'s treasure for more
than half a century.

When the weather had moderated, the schooner's captain
bellowed, "Up anchor!" Men strained to lift the 400-pound

hook but without success; it was fouled in something on the bottom. A Malayan foremast hand, once a pearl diver, volunteered to go down to investigate. He discovered that one of the anchor flukes was held by what appeared to be a massive chain heavily encrusted with sea growth and a conglomerate mass of mud, rust and a black substance that was probably disintegrated gun powder. Nearby was a mysterious object resembling a huge bell. After a series of dives he succeeded in getting a line around it so that it could be hoisted to the surface and on board the schooner. Then he followed the chain along the bottom of which it was now almost an integral part. It led to what had once been a ship. Time and the sea had left but little more than the keel and a few rotted ribs.

Impossible to dislodge, the schooner's anchor was abandoned. Sail was made and running wing-and-wing, the trading vessel scudded away before a spanking breeze. Later in the day the mate set the Malayan to chipping the heavy marine growth from the recovered bell. After a couple of hours' work with scraper and sandstone it was gleaming in the declining sunlight. On its surface in raised letters was the legend "H. M. S. LUTINE."

Unaware of the importance of their find, captain and crew made no secret of where and how they secured the bell. Word that the true *Lutine* had been discovered spread like summer heat lightning and again the hunt for gold was on. Dutch fishermen were first on the scene, but without adequate salvage equipment their time and effort were wasted. Then on various occasions professional salvors arrived with dredges and other devices for the recovery of the treasure. All attempts were fruitless.

Lloyd's of London, in spite of international agreement, never surrendered the ownership of the gold. Their position was sustained by the British Government so vigorously that on one occasion it sent a detachment of marines to disperse a flotilla of fishing craft bent on harvesting the *Lutine's* treasure.

An English salvage concern, by arrangement with Lloyd's, entered the spirited contest. Equipped with the most modern diving and dredging apparatus, it actually succeeded in recovering gold and silver valued at $100,000.

In 1898, another British company carried on salvage for several years without success. Its divers found that mud, sand and silt from previous operations had been washed to a great depth over the wreck by storms and tides.

In 1907, Lloyd's in desperation called in the well-known American submarine engineer, Simon Lake, to devise a means of recovering the *Lutine's* gold. His ingenuity challenged, Lake invented a steel tube or shaft through which men could descend to a steel chamber on the bottom. Equipped with powerful search-lights, observation windows and telephone to the dredge on the surface, it was in a sense a kind of diving shell from which the work of the dredge could be directed. The plans were drawn, construction was begun and the prospects of success were never brighter.

Then one day, as in the case of the *Florencia*, World War I engulfed the civilized world. Again the buried gold was forgotten as so much dross. The lives and liberty of peoples were all that mattered. Compared with the billions spent during the succeeding war years, the *Lutine's* golden hoard was but a widow's mite dropped into the sea and buried deep down under.

THE END